PALABRITAS

Vol 1. Issue 1 (2020-2021)

PALABRITAS ANNUAL TEAM
Fall & Spring (2020-2021)

Editor-in-Chief
Rosa Flores-Rueda

Managing Editor
Ryan Morillo

Multimedia & Design
Daniela Bolanos

Readers & Editors

Ada Cruz	Joselyn Vera	Felipe Munoz
Sammantha Garcia	Yasmeen Alfaqueeh	Hannah Martinez
Fatima Reyes	Emily Rios	Penelope Alegria
Noelle Castro		

Cover art courtesy of Jocelyn Hassel

Dedicated to everyone we have lost in the last year and half at the hands of COVID-19, police brutality and Asian hate crimes.

CONTENTS

ARTIST'S NOTE ON COVER ART

There are two things that are especially significant for me about this piece: motherhood and celebration of hair, both of which are rooted in Blackness. I found this image of the mother and child as a vintage ad for Black hair products in the United States, celebrating afros as a generational project. The basis of this art was a form of healing for me, specifically in terms of presence/absence of these themes in my own personal life. At the root of it is my identity as being raised by a Dominican single mother who is visibly Black and therefore, a Black Dominican woman (as not all Dominicans are Black - and of course there is that underlying sense of anti-Blackness in the Dominican Republic where asserting Blackness, even for Black Dominicans, could be contentious for some people). Although I am half white (my father being a white American who encapsulates everything about American empire that has produced enormous trauma for my mother), being raised only by my mother and experiencing the resilience of motherhood, informed my own upbringing and my leaning into feminism that is decolonial, from the Global South, and rooted in liberation for all. My hair has been a significant source of my identity, but also a site of contestations of anti-Black formations. Celebrating natural hair in spite of respectability politics and the hair straightening complex has been incredibly important to me and has also been the source of academic writing for me in law school. The process of larger conversations on unlearning internalized trauma rooted in anti-Blackness in the Dominican Republic has been a powerful movement to witness and has also been such a huge part of my work in Black liberation as a tenant advocate, an abolitionist, and an artist. My collage art has been a way for me to tap into Blackness and to ensure that the viewer does not automatically relegate this assertion of Blackness as somehow "separate" from what has been the harmful monolith of Latinidad. It is this monolith that has prevented my own family from having intentional conversations on Blackness, simply equating Latinx as a racial category, and therefore, ignoring that the visible Blackness of my own family is the site of a racial identity tied to Dominican ethnicity and national identity. This art piece is a form of healing, of collective care, and a continual fight against white supremacy and colonial memory in all of its forms.

My collage has centered this imagery and infused it with traditional Caribbean imagery - vivacious plants, parrots, colorful images that resemble the pastel-colored houses that spotted my own family's neighborhood in San Francisco de Macorís. I miss it every day. Being raised by a single mother, and therefore being raised upon Dominican cultural tradition, has carried so much significance for me as I navigate the ivory tower regime as a first-gen student and soon-to-be lawyer/scholar-activist, and the constant white spaces that attempt to force Black and brown folks to contest their belonging. I carry this identity and use it to fuel a larger desire for collective liberation in uprooting the forms of hegemony that have made life so difficult for my mother, for my family, for my Black and brown brothers and sisters.

Jocelyn Hassel
Cambridge, MA
April 16, 2021

POETRY

FLAVORFUL INK
Aleyda Cervantes

Poetry is not about rhymes and words.

I love it more than I like theory,
Perhaps more than fiction
Definitely more than science.

It is a body made of experiences
A hyperbole, an anecdote
An illusion of a passion
Pictures smashing together
Sexual and not sexual
It is a lotus flower
Other times a nopal in the dessert.
Poetry has no gender
No nationality
No home

Poetry is not for the rich
It is not for the privilege
It is not for those who don't.

You won't find it in a hipster coffee shop with metal chairs.
You won't find it during an expensive class with professor making
you feel small, stupid, inadequate.
You won't find it in the 100 dollar notebooks or the big publishers.

Poetry is what screams inside of us.

In the middle of the fields, between pesticides and long hours.

In the receipts of what others, buy but we can't ever afford.
In sticky notes, of the jobs that feed us.
In the jars of the food we don't eat.

Poetry speaks back to us. Using all languages. Using no language.
Poetry is a collection of anything and beyond.
Poetry is the memory of this world.

So I praise poetry and the poet.
I praise those who read it and don't judge it.
I praise those who play it
      Wreck-it, Destroy it. Who judge it again.
I praise those of us who know.
    Who find
        poetry written in traces
                and
                  fragments

Staying in the past and
moves silently into the
future. In poetry, we
live.
In death, we poetry.

Poetry is poetry.
A poem is a song of civilization.
We are the poets,
And poets
    we do what we want.

AMERICA, THE CONTINENT
Mayte Castro

Recall the stories passed down!
Shatter the mouth guard of erasure.

> Present the African and Indigenous resilience
> on the canvas showcasing America
> the continent.

Recall the stories passed down.
Far from the flaw-focused,
challenging and obstructive
muddles.

> Histories live in many forms
> Finding an abode within conversations
> across generations.

Recall the stories passed down.

> In the kitchen, alongside the fire pit,
> in the lullabies
> across languages of America
> The continent.

Recall the stories passed down.

> Daring as La Llorona under her veils
> Well-known for her moves.
> Never receiving a doubtful glance,
> Or teetering on disbelief.

Recall the stories passed down.

Intellectual as Sor Juana Inés de la Cruz
Perceptive to the value of an education.

Recall the stories passed down.

Malinche's shawl
Gushing from it the open
wounds of the indigenous.
Appearing appealing, such tainted item
Museums would acquiesce,
In a flash!

Recall the stories passed down.

Crestfallen Queen Isabel carries
many masks that weigh forever more
over the stolen jewels, lives, and existence
of far too many.

Recall the stories passed down.
Remember, histories live
in many
forms.
Finding an abode within conversations
across
generations.

In the kitchen, alongside the fire pit,
in the lullabies
across languages of America.
The continent recalls its stories passed down.

MY ANTITHESIS
Ramon Jimenez

We cannot live together ever.
Nor would I dare share a meal
and break bread with you on Thanksgiving
or crack cold ones on the 4th of July
or any other holiday that reminds me of your subjugation.

We do not want the same things.
You want borders and order,
reverence for the men in uniform.
We want freedom of movement
and human rights to those denied for a century and greater
just like we want those kids liberated from those filthy cages.
After all, if you don't want us here why keep us around?

We want to have peace and live in it,
but you want war
guns and ammunition sweating through your pores.
You claim to have the whole US constitution memorized,
but it seems that you only have the 2nd memorized
while you pour mud over the 14th.

Where I see family,
you see crime, terror, and threats.
Where I see a community doing its best to survive,
you see a disgusting and dangerous ghetto that needs to be violently
cracked down.
Bulldozed and gentrified so that you can feel safe enough to walk
your dog, Piper.

You are what I am not
and so, we will never heal this divide.
Our differences will never be sealed, settled or mended
over tea and pastries.
Like that stupid wall you wish to construct,
a division of hot cement and pointy barbed wire will separate us
forever.
This will only end one way.

EL SENDERO
Dulce Mata

Es aquel sendero
el que muchos han transitado,
el triste camino arduo
en el que varios se han quedado.

Es aquel sendero
el que conoce las plegarias,
las lagrimas y escasas risas
de aquellas almas perdidas y gregarias.

Es aquel sendero
en el que huellas yacen a diario,
aquellas que con fulgor han pintado
los nómadas transitando hacia su calvario.

Es aquel sendero
el que ansioso observa al hombre
caminar al compás del sol vívido,
sin tener la dicha de conocer su nombre.

Es aquel sendero
el que espera en paz al próximo viajero,
fiel inmigrante soñador afligido
con hambre del triunfo y alma de acero.

Es aquel sendero
el que, sin entender el porqué de su papel,
sigue siendo la vereda que se dice
ha conducido al paisano a un destino cruel.

FAMILIA
Hannah Martinez

Why did you not gift me with your tongue?
Why did you look at me as a child
And say good morning instead of buenos días,
Tell me to wash my hands instead of lávarte las manos,
And bar me from your language?

And don't you know?
Every time someone sees my skin, my melanin
They start rambling in *your tongue*
A language I cannot speak
And I stand there like a fool, guilt in my chest
The forbidden tongue trying to escape my throat and it *can't*
Because all I know to say in my halting, broken Spanish
Tainted by a white accent is
no hablo español.
My cheeks run hot as the words spill out
Like unfamiliar marbles through gritted teeth.
I feel like a fraud.

And they'll ask, oh they'll ask.
¿Porque no te hablas?
I'm trying,
I'm trying to conjugate and remember my lessons
Duolingo, Spanish classes, Rosetta fucking Stone
The brown girl who speaks the foreigner's tongue
The brown girl who looks Hispanic but
What kind of Hispanic can't even speak Spanish?
And as I stand there and mourn the conversation
In rapid-fire español
That I will not have,

8

I am mourning palabritas I never even knew.

THE SUN Y LA LUNA
Briana Maytee García

I am the Sun.
Been shining bright since the day I was born,
praised for consistency, pronunciation, recognition.

Yo soy la Luna.
También he iluminado la noche desde mi principio,
todos me miraban en admiración por saber tanto.

The world is awake to see the Sun.
My glittering rays represent endless possibility and opportunity:
Prosperous education, patriotism, formality, respect, superiority--
enough!
The Sun's searing powers do not please all populations.

> *Why don't you come out at night?*
> *Do you have to be so hot?*
> *I bet that's all you know how to do, how to be a golden sun.*
> *Aren't you a little dark to be a Sun?*

I wish I could always be the moon.

El mundo está dormido cuando sale la Luna.
Soy la luz en la oscuridad, la poderosa esperanza para los perdidos;
hablar con mis parientes, sobresalir ante la competencia, tener
cultura--¿y al final de cuentas, ¿qué significa eso?
No le agrada la Luna a todos.

> *¿Por qué no sales todo el tiempo?*
> *Ni te enseñas ante gente importante.*

¿Por qué no puedes ser como nosotros?
No puedes hablar bien, te crees como si fueras de aquí de verdad.
Mírate, el nopal en la frente, que no se te olvide.

Como me gustaría ser el Sol todo el tiempo.

I am the Sun, I adore her.
The system wants the Sun, the Sun they will have.
También soy la Luna, ella me define.
La raza quiere la Luna, la Luna tendrá.

      Listen here readers, sí estoy hablando con ustedes.
You can be the Sun, it's okay. When you go to school, get a job, vote-
- you can be the Sun.
Puedes ser la Luna, está bien. Cuando estés con la familia, con tu
gente--puedes ser la Luna.

CENTRAL AMERICAN SAVAGERY
Steve Castro

"I wish I were a man," my mother told me in Spanish,
"because then I would have been able to defend
that helpless dog." She then told me how
when she was on vacation in Nicaragua, in broad daylight,
at a public park in front of a number of bystanders,
a man picked up a stick and started
beating a dog to death for no reason.
My mother was visibly upset while telling me this story.
As a man, I wonder what I would have done.
I probably would have watched from a safe distance,
wishing I had Athena's courage to intervene.

COMAL
Alyssa Noelle Patiño Krull

A round tortilla sizzles
Masa puffs into air pockets
Abuela tells you, "No toques"
And proceeds to touch the rising tortilla
Her hands have been hardened
Her calluses refined
She can reach into fire
Yet not be burned
Why do you poke at it abuela?
"Because your Nana did
And so did Grandma Francis
That's how it has always been
And always will be"
She stacks the final tortilla
On the growing pile next to the stove
She hands me one
And shows me how to eat it properly
Dip it into her dangerously spicy chile con carne
"Your mother can't handle the spice
But you can"
I blush with pride
I am my grandmother's nieta
My roots reach deep into México
And yet the only connection that remains
Is my Nana's comal

MI MEXICO LINDO
America Garcia

Poderosas máquinas de puro calor
Que no dejan de arder de el poder que tienen,
De gente que quiere más y que nunca dejan de pelear,
Que además de trabajadores
tienen el corazón para no solo hacer lo
Que hacen todo lo que se propongan;
De levantarse para levantar a los niños,
A hacerles los lonches para la escuela, Hasta de vivir de la pecera por
toda la ciudad,
De ir devuelta para
Hacer pagos de agua, luz, y gas
De lavar los trastes y los uniformes de los niños y recoger toda la
casa,
De hasta ayudar a los niños con la tarea,
De hacer todo de comer,
De poner todo en orden
Que en verdad no hay un descanso
Que se sienta vivo y puro
Literalmente los pies no se les paran y así de orgullosa
Soy de la gente potente
                 fuerte
                 y pudiente

COMO ANUNCIACIÓN LO HACÍA

Ana Lorenza Jimenez

Grandma,
give me a cleansing?

brush my body
with the branches
of the willow, rosemary, and rue

rub my skin
with a raw unbroken egg

anoint me
with the fragrant Florida water

how you pour the perfume from
the ornate long-necked bottle
into your hands with assertion
and flick your fingers around me

with the same power in your fingers
It is drawn out of me
absorbed
into the egg

broken

and It
dispelled by the cross

read a psalm

and whisper a prayer

the way your Apache mother used to

Grandma,
give me a cleansing

beat It
out of me
with branches of
pirul, romero, and ruda

huevo rompiendo

bipolaridad debajo de la cruz

Abuelita,
dame una limpieza dura

empápame con agua
de florida
como las lluvias
atormentan el desierto

declara un salmo tan fuerte
dilo rápido y suavemente

en menos tiempo
que bipolaridad tiene
para cambiar mi mente
Abuelita, dame una limpieza

como tu mamá, Anunciación lo hacía

WHEN I LEARNED TO SPEAK UP
Gabriella Nayeli Salvador

It was the condescending *"Hola"*
 as I walked into my honors English class—
Or was it the way no one ate my mother's mole at the cultural
potluck?
Was it the way I rolled the r's when I said my name?
"Why are you so quiet?"
Was it the way I unknowingly wore the love of my indigenous culture
on my sleeve or
was it my stinging silence in the classroom?
They couldn't pick which one made them more
uncomfortable.
Regardless, I was different
and different was not normal.
My younger self asked "what is normal?"
Well, normal is white.
And white was not the indigenous language spoken in my home.
White was not rolling my r's when saying my own name.
Gabriella Nayeli Salvador.
"Wait what, Naye- that's *weird*"
Nayeli—It means I love you in a tongue unimportant to you.
Nayeli, spoken by my ancestors, the Zapotec people.
Ironically, I cannot love myself when I am not normal
Because I am not a reflection of beauty in this country.
Because my brown skin speaks louder than my actual voice.
Because in the classroom, smart isn't smart enough for you to
listen to me.
And still they ask me,
"Why are you so quiet?"

INTERSECTIONALITY
Delia Wallace

I am exactly who I was meant to be
On a day like today
Yet somehow, I feel incomplete
Displaced and confused by the desire to see
To be seen and felt by those like me

There is privilege in belonging seamlessly
In having all of your parts fit into a category
I search for privilege in this skin
I carve it with this tongue
I hope for both more and less at the same time

I wear my names proudly
Each one separately, that is
Because it still stings to answer questions like
"Are you Black or Latina?"
"Are you gay or straight?"
"Are you religious or spiritual?"

As if I cannot be all of these things at once

ABUE GILA

Theresa Palafox

Abue Gila gave birth to 12 children and raised the additional two that were left on her doorstep.

Her head, molded to the flatness of the breadbasket she carried from 7am till she sold out.

"El pan! Pan!"

She chanted thru the narrow alleys that smelled so dirty no one was longer bothered by it.

Abue knew how to make tummies feel better with Yerba Buena. She let it steep just enough to get the nutrients out before destroying the leaves, adding the right amount of sweetener to Make it tolerable to drink.

"Ati te hicieron mal"

People like her knew when a malicious spirit had penetrated the body.

People like her also cured it.

Rosemary, albaca, and lavender. 2 huevos cafeces de gallina de granja y muchos Padres Nuestros. One after the other in a cross motion across the body.

Shaking the negative energy away.

"En el nombre del padre, del hijo..." silently under her breath, still praying.

Abue said para todo hay algo

I've been trying to learn in my dreams ever since.

TAGGING
Cynthia Alicia Flores

On a concrete wall, a boy with a paint can
Frosts the names of the lost ones. Zigzag serifs drift
Into the masonry, a mortared page for the powerless.
Here, in the arid hours of zero below grief,
Landscapes of snow have become our longing.
We have never bowled ice in the concave of our palms
Nor seen the snowfall smear into a blizzard of blank.
Still - we know cold and speak it with faith.
There is a place, a far-off country, where everything is white.
The village snow there is punctured, the boot tracings
Of a fading farewell. But here, the record of absence
Is a different design   Slim cars recede and darken
Into the Avenues, as glyphs remain, - shadowy and barbed -
To ease our forgetting, to provoke wars of our memory.

OLD GAS STATION
German Piedrahita

paint and shine barely holding
to its chemical attachment

clouded glass keeps
            anachronistic treasures
the street plays its music
wind dust patronizes

in knee deep weeds sits the old station
time   a daydream passed   you

in the stillness

with passing cars the place comes alive
            like muscle memory of phantom limbs

the bell over the door never stops
whispering   hellos   and   farewells

UNDOCUMENTED MEDICINE
Jesus Cortez

This poem should be ingested
once every morning,
for as long as you have
that nauseating feeling of
blind faith in the so-called
American dream—

      I would let it burn,
along with the rest of the monuments
to "white supremacy"—
they gotta remind you of that
constantly, and you love the white
supremacists, and you hide it in your brain
and you hide it in your soul,
and you worry that white america
may stop loving you if you take
the colonizer out your head—
so you stood for the flag,
as they invaded the "Third World",
as they invaded the moon
and you didn't mind it flying
above Abu Ghraib and
above Guantanamo,
as they tortured your Brown
and Black "enemies" to defend the freedom
to kill you on the streets, as their uniforms
carry that same bloody flag.

Side effects may include:
delusions of freedom,

the audacity to feel like
speaking truth to power,
and possibly rage—

      I pledge allegiance to the
descendants of Teresa,
and their descendants

I pledge allegiance to my
streets, across Anaheim,
where dreams are broken

I pledge allegiance donut
shop coffee and donuts,
and tacos and burritos,
I pledge allegiance to my
heart, broken but growing
and shared with few

I pledge allegiance to my soul
impure, perhaps, but mine
after all

I pledge allegiance to no flag
and no nation and no man
and nobody unworthy of me.

PROSE

WHEN I WAS BRAVE
Ednin D. Martinez

I finished speaking to my client at the county jail, exited the interview room in that pod, and walked into the small area between the interview room and the exit door. I pushed the button to alert the guard that I was done and waited for him to let me out. Behind me was a second door, but that one was floor to ceiling glass. Through the glass, I could see inmates watching me wait while in the common area of the pod.

It was a cold late December afternoon, and although I'd have a break coming up for the holidays all I could think of was the piles of work that waited for me at the office. I pushed the button again and made eye contact with the guard throwing both hands in the air while sucking my teeth. As the door in front of me began to open, I heard a muffled voice coming from behind me through the glass door.

"Mami chula, morena. Te voy agarrar ese culo y te voy a meter el dedo paya dentro, a que te gusta que te lo metan asi."

While he intricately described how he would put his fingers inside me, the door opened wide enough for me to squirm out. I stepped into a cloud of bleach in the hospital like sterile hallway. The fumes and halogen lights closed in on me. I was dizzy. My legs felt heavy, but I managed to move forward. My heart drummed loudly in my chest as I sped up the pace. Out of breath, I reached the outside of the county jail and inhaled crisp winter air until my lungs were full. My eyes welled up with tears that stung as I sobbed violently.

I had convinced myself that these were just snippets of this life. *My* life. At first, being a public defender was honorable, fulfilling work. I was protecting constitutional rights. Making a difference. But what I didn't know was that there would come a point I'd have to front like I was enjoying my job while it wreaked havoc on my soul. But I continued pretending to be the savior, while in desperate need of saving.

My colleagues and clients were mostly male; I felt disposable in that world. Let's keep it real, I was a public defender, so if a client got a hold of a few thousand dollars to pay for a private attorney they'd replace me in a heartbeat. They'd hire a slick haired, pinstripe-suit wearing, older white man. And if they didn't, then they made sure they got everything they needed out of me.

It didn't matter that I was their lawyer, because I was a woman, they'd assert their masculinity and remind me who was in charge at every turn. Do and say shit they'd never get away with if they were represented by a man.

So, it wasn't just the "Yo! She got a fat ass!" comments at the jail and sometimes in court that got to me. It was the repulsive looks that reduced me to a set of walking nalgas and tetas that made me want to crawl back into my skin. It was the lack of respect for me as a lawyer, a woman. A black Latina woman. They didn't have to respect me. But it was their failure to see that I believed in this work; in their rights, and their refusal to acknowledge *I* was also human which was most exhausting.

This job was my first real job as a lawyer. For the first five years of my career, I felt like I was an outsider looking in. I went through the motions and took the abuse.

My second year in the office, I was preparing for what would be my third trial and met with my client at the jail to explain his options and trial strategy. I tried to convince him of my qualifications to represent him, but also had to endure his comments about my age, my legal skills and my body.

"Yo miss, how many trials have you done... I mean, you seem mad young, are you *really* gonna fight for me?"

I took a deep breath, held it a few seconds and exhaled. I forced a smile and explained how many jury trials I had under my belt, years of experience, the types of motions I had filed, and on and on. I spoke until I convinced him and maybe even myself, that I could do the job. Once he thought we were cool, the real fun began.

"Not for nothing, but I need to get this out of the way, you're mad thick. How come I don't see no ring on your finger?"

I had enough. "Sir, this is completely inappropriate. I am here to speak to you about your case and the evidence or lack-thereof. I am here to discuss a possible defense strategy. When you are ready to talk about *that* let me know."

He managed to muster a "my bad" as I let myself out of the interview room, fuming. But I didn't tell anyone. This happened again and again. The more I let it happen, the more I felt trapped in this abusive cycle.

***

What happened my first month at the job was a sign of things to come and should have warned me.

It was a typical Monday morning with a heavy calendar, sometimes I had fifteen to twenty cases in one day. The court was full of frustrated clients that needed my attention, and some waited for me in the holding cell. I walked down to the musty basement jail, sat down on a torn chocolate pleather couch and waited my turn. When the guard called "next!" I leapt up and walked into the wannabe foyer.

Looking through the paint chipped iron bars, I greeted the guard, showed him my badge and told him who I needed to speak to. He called out my client's name, who acknowledged he was there. The electronic bars in his cell clinked loudly as they opened to let him out. I made my way further inside. The crowd of inmates erupted in laughter as I passed them.

One guy teased my client: "Yo! That's your lawyer?"

I was already annoyed but put on a poker face and kept it moving.

The urine filled air hit my nostrils as I passed the only bathroom downstairs. I tried not to gag and took my place in the makeshift interview room, sat near an old wooden desk and plopped my plea forms on top. My client sat across from me in a plastic, navy-blue chair, facing the brick wall behind me. He blocked the only exit.

I got to work. I took each form from the desk and placed it on my lap as I asked him questions.

"Are you pleading guilty because you are guilty?" "Are you under the influence of any drugs that could impair your ability to make a decision to plead guilty today?"

In the middle of the interview, I heard heavy breathing. *Something's not right.* I looked up from the pile of papers to his big frame, *is this manganzón hyperventilating?*

"Uh—please, take a deep breath. You—um, you don't have to take this offer. Remember you…you have a right to a trial okay?"

I was clueless.

But he knew exactly what he was doing. He looked into my eyes with a crooked smile and pointed at the bulge on his crotch with a handcuffed hand.

"It's just, it's been so long…" he said unaffected, as I almost fell over in my chair. I finished the interview, straightened and paper-clipped the forms, got up, walked past him and went back to court. As I took the elevator up, sweat beads dripped down my back.

***

When I took this job almost six years before, I had no idea I'd have to turn to stone on a daily basis or make all these concessions *just-to-get-work-done*. I had to wear clothes that were less form fitting, be less friendly so that I wouldn't be perceived as weak. It was incessant, but things didn't get better.

One day I broke my own rules, I dared to wear a form-fitting, plum pantsuit to court. I felt powerful, even confident in it. I liked how it skimmed my thighs and accentuated my waist. *Pa qué fue eso*, because halfway through the morning calendar my colleague caught a man in the back of the courtroom recording my butt on his phone. A sheriff's officer ran after him, took the phone and deleted the videos. It could have been worse.

I set myself up for that one, that was all me.

Back at the office, I thought about swimming in one of my ex's sweatpants and sprawling out on my couch. Oh, and Riesling, lots of Riesling. I never wore that suit again.

***

I was a scrawny kid but developed thighs and ass as a teen and decided to run cross country in high school to try to hide them. They were always the culprits of unwanted attention making me want to become invisible. That trend did not improve with time. At the private, predominantly white college I attended, my curves stood out. I was one of the only Black Latinas and sometimes the only person of color in every single one of my classes. Law school, same.

Then I started this job and thought somehow, I was protected by some sort of colorblind bubble. The fact was, for almost six years I felt paralyzed by how I was treated, swallowed my anger and pushed it down. Every comment about my body, my race or ethnicity, every year that passed, the anger accumulated, until it boiled like lava in the pit of my belly. The longer I stayed the more I wanted out.

***

That day as I waited to exit that pod, that inmate's words hit a nerve. The malice in his tone, how he uttered vulgarities to me in my native tongue, sucked all the air out of my lungs.

His words were vile, so much that they catapulted me to when I was a girl of six or seven.

It was pitch-black in that room at Mamá's house when I woke up to the sound of crickets outside my window and the feeling of being crushed by his sweaty naked weight. He rubbed up and down the outside of my pajamas and moved fast. I screamed with all the strength I could muster as he pressed my mouth down with a clammy hand. I kicked, pushed and bit his fingers, until he let me go. I was a warrior that night.

I bolted out of that room in the back of the house into the hallway. I tried running straight to Mamá's room but saw that I was trapped. There was a wooden door Mamá only closed at night. It separated the new part of the house from the old. The door had a rusty lock at the very top. Then, I remembered the bathroom was the only other way out. I scurried through it into my tia's bedroom, which connected to Mamá's room and felt the cool tile beneath my feet.

I sobbed hysterically and bumped my little legs into hard surfaces trying to find my way in the dark until I reached Mamá's room. She turned the lights on, and for the first time I saw fear on the face of a woman who'd raised eleven children on her own.

"Pero mi hija, ¿qué fue lo que pasó?" She said questioning what had happened, and I somehow explained. She held me until I fell asleep in her arms.

My parents had separated a few weeks before and sent my sister to La Capital with my maternal grandmother. I got to stay with Mamá and Papi in San Pedro. I was homesick. I missed waking up to the comforting scent of Mami's yanikeke and hot chocolate made from scratch. This wasn't my home.

The next day I woke up thinking I'd had a nightmare. On the days after this incident, for many nights, I dreamt of monsters chasing me and woke up crying in Mamá's bed. But this was no dream.

That morning, I saw him as he stood there in the middle of that hallway from the night before. His brown naked body glistened against the green ceramic tile he stood on. His older brothers (my uncles) towered over him with black leather belts and worn wooden broomsticks. They beat him until his tears ran out.

I thought I'd forgiven him and moved on with my life, but years later, I remembered that night like a 3-D movie. I continued to excuse his actions as those of a schizophrenic teenage boy.

I did not realize when it was I lost my grit. But it was without doubt during those years my parents taught me to act like a lady, curve my reactions, let things go.

They'd often say:

"Las niñas don't get into fights, or raise their voice, or talk back."

But they had no idea they were stripping me of the courage I would need later in life.

31

Although there are defining moments when the courageous little girl made her way out, I realize that when I needed her most, when I needed to stand up for myself, she was gently tucked away. So– I didn't dare conjure up that childhood memory on purpose, it was painful. But the girl I was that night, the one who fought back, the one who saved herself, that's the girl I'm looking for. That warrior girl. I feel her at times, making her way back, but struggle to let her be brave.

AFROARGENTINXS ARE REAL, ARGENTINA IS JUST RACIST.

Martina Palavecino Bó
Nonfiction

On June 24th, 2020 Walter Ceferino Nadal was stopped by two police officers in my hometown after being accused of stealing a baseball cap from a supermarket. They brought him down on the street, one officer put his knee on his neck. Ceferino Nadal yelled, "me falta el aire". Ceferino Nadal was murdered at 43 years old on the hands of two police officers who attributed themselves the role of executioners. He was killed by a knee to the neck in the name of a baseball cap.

Only a month after George Floyd, mi San Miguel de Tucumán witnessed the death of Nadal. *Me falta el aire* became a fancy title for the media to feel closer to los Estados Unidos and capitalize on the murder of an innocent man. In the land of peronismo de la justicia social, the murders of people of color in Argentina are perceived to be just justice working properly. While protests flooded the streets in los Estados Unidos, my town could not help but celebrate the death of another "lacra."

Lower income individuals in Argentina are called black. Their place in our society is "fuera de las calles" because la calle is the space for honest people; prison should be the space for "lacras." Being "out of the streets" here means being unable to steal from the middle and upper classes. In Tucumán, it is believed that society itself should take undesired people out of the streets in case the government fails to do so. Given our history with military governments taking people out of the street, with their detention ending in murder, prison and death have become the way conservative citizens end the problem with "lacras." Consequently, people enjoyed the fact that another black man was removed from the streets. The main publication in Tucumán, La

Gaceta, ran multiple articles about the death of Nadal. Each one is filled with upvoted comments taking the side of the police officers and celebrating the death of a man, una muerte que significa un delincuente fuera de las calles.

I will say black, abstaining from using the Spanish word, given the hatred it spatters out of my people's mouth. The word carries the weight of centuries of the deepest odio. It carries the history of oppression, the past of putting people of color on the battlefields to sacrifice them, the forgotten memory of the places where people from "África" were brought to "América" to be sold into slavery.

La palabra, configurante de mundos, de sentidos, tiene el peso de haber silenciado en su historia al afroargentinx. Argentina decidió esta configuración al consolidarse como una nación con pretensión europea, a tal punto que la palabra afroargentinxs resulta inconcebible aquí. Argentinians deeply and truly believe that Argentina is not a Latin American nation with people of color. That is because they only consider themselves as a white nation with some mestizaje, left behind generations ago and genetically closer to Europeans.Argentina es la París de América Latina, Argentina es casi europea, Argentina es prácticamente italiana y española. As Gisele Kleidermacher implies to in "Africanos y Afrodescendientes en Argentina", we sell ourselves as the whitest people in América Latina.

We are, perhaps, the most disliked nationality in América del Sur. Everyone around us hates us, as Gladys Adamson, director of Escuela de Psicología Social del Sur, alludes to on an interview with BBC.

Argentinians, for sure, go out of their way to express hate towards other countries. Bolivianx, paraguayx, brasilerx, peruanx are not nationalities in Argentina; they are insults filled with disgust. We do, indeed, deserve our neighbor's hate. We consider them non-white nations, Alejandro Grimson suggests in "-Nuevas xenofobias, nuevas políticas étnicas en Argentina"; therefore, people of color in Argentina are called bolivianx, paraguayxs, and so on.

There is this famous joke made in other countries: "¿Cómo se suicida un argentinx? Lx tiras de su propio ego." Well, they are right. Pope Francis made this joke on an interview on March 2015, referring to how arrogant and nationalists Argentinians are. Our egos are built on centuries of exclusion of "minorías" and decades of orgullo argentino. Messi, Maradona, asado, supremacía blanca y europeizante. Tango, which came from afroargentinxs, is usually associated with our nation. Yet, since Argentina considers itself to be a white nation where afro and argentinx identities are incompatible, tango has been appropriated as a cultural expression from white Argentinians for white Argentinians. You are argentinx or you are afro.

"Afroargentinxs no hay, toda la gente de África acá se murió en las guerras o con la fiebre amarilla," they tell us. "There's no racism here," they say. They are sure of it: escuchás la seguridad en sus voces. Here, there are no African descents. They call white people "black" if they are poor or represent the "lacras" in our society. Therefore, we cannot be racist. We are beyond racism, they say, given that skin color isn't used as a primary tool to systematically exclude and oppress our people.
We are beyond racism, they protest, because if you were ever to encounter un afroargentinx on the street, you will know that they are simply not argentinxs. They came from somewhere far away, even if their family has lived in Argentina for generations. We will never believe it because we are the whitest latinxs, because we honestly believe ourselves to be european.

Interseccionalidad in our nationality only counts si sos italiano, español, si sos europeo. Si sos indígena, les querés robar la tierra, pero si sos afroargentinx, no sos **nada**.

Interseccionalidad is a cute thing that white feminists say while also singing racist terms in protests. Interseccionalidad is a term used by Argentinian Academia to look good to others, while frequently finding the same Academia defending our nation's racism. They will cross all limits to excuse racist art, racist writing, racist scandals, and they will actively ignore and deny afroargentinxs defending their identity and existence. For example, in November 2020, the Museo de Arte Latinoamericano de Buenos Aires posted on Instagram images of a racist past art performance, depicting people doing blackface inside cages, imitating a zoo, months after offering a course on art and racism. The institution defended itself after backlash explaining it was not racist: it was meant to teach about racism. Yet, it did not teach, explain, or invite meditation about the subject.

If being part of Argentinian Academia means supporting white supremacy in my country, I am no longer certain of my future in it. The erasure of afroargentinian history in my country starts at the core of the discourse and actions in Academia. Silence and denial have been allies of the oppression afroargentinxs suffer. They are still the tools that maintain the racist structure. Academics teach history and reproduce white nationalist discourses in class, use them as the essence of the theory of their thesis. They use their privileged places to sustain a system that excludes identities. As a white Argentinian woman, I choose not to partake in this Academia. Not being racist is not enough -- being antiracism is the bare minimum we, the oppressors, can do.

Argentina is not white, Argentina is just profundamente y odiosamente racista. Interseccionalidad is not a token word to fit in the future of Academia; interseccionalidad es reconocer las identidades afroargentinxs y otorgar las herramientas para reconocerse frente al espejo.

No hay otra forma de entenderlo: ellxs son afroargentinxs, y vos, racista.

MCNÍFICA

By Eric Ponce

   McDonalds in South America has a sandwich called the McNífica. "Es más que buena, es magnífica," the TV sings, the same Spanish cadence as my grandfather. In Lima, Peru there are only (only) about 20 McDonalds restaurants. My Quiteño cousin who studied in Lima told me that McDonalds is hip and ginchy (my mother's translations) over there, like how we saw In-N-Out when it first came to Texas.

When we drove up to the red and white nostalgia building and stood in line behind a large loud family, he asked me if In-N-Out had an equivalent to the McNífica. I told him I didn't know and he explained the sandwich to me. It sounded like a regular burger.

We sat in our booth and waited for our number. He'd only been with us a day and already we were running out of conversation topics—his English was as bad as my Spanish. My Noam Chomsky poster gave us some gas for the first day but now here we were, Chomsky'd out.

We sat for a bit sipping soda until he told me about this one Mickey D's he went to in Pueblo Libre, a little ways from where he was staying as he studied linguistics. He said he'd go there on the weekends and get a McNífica (no one on my mother's side has the stature or stomach for a true Big Mac) and talk to the two kids who worked there. He told me their names were Alexandra and Gabriel.

They used to date, but then they decided to just be friends. Decided is a harsh word though, too real, too much responsibility. Gabriel still harbored feelings for her, deep and hot and bubbling, like the deep fryer he plunged cold cardboardy "potatoes" in, he thought. Like the papas, he came out steaming and tender and pithy to the bite. He kept the job because she kept the job. Yes, they did see each other at work every day, and they still had all the same same friends, and they lived close by but he still missed it, he missed her—the kind of secret language that came with a relationship. The looks and the touches, effused with a different kind of light, that no one else can see, only you. You create something together, make it real to you. She hadn't been his girlfriend for that long but when she had it was like everything was neon, bright as the golden arches over him.

She felt somewhat contra to this, and he knew it. They both knew it, and the pressure of that it was her "fault" that they were no longer an item was a lot to handle for her, naturally. Especially because she had to see him every day not just around the neighborhood but at work, where there was a double level of pressure, stacked high and topped with sesame seeds. She didn't want to have a boyfriend, to have another obligation to someone that she wasn't sure she could keep, and so she told him. I still care about you, and I hope we can still be friends. It was all in the words.

They were out of school now and saving for college, which is how my cousin befriended them. Young people, the same age, no matter class or race, usually bond over something. For them it was French fries.

The lady at the counter called our number, my cousin got up but I insisted. When I sat back down with the steaming bright red tray, he had gotten little white cups of ketchup. For the fries, he said. We started eating.

He told me about their relationship more. How Gabriel would talk to him about her. He'd get a French fry and wax about how good warm fries are, golden crunchy salty, y'know? But if you left the golden rods sit eventually they'd get cold. A weird mix of hard and mushy, light years different from the warm fry. In a matter of minutes, the fry transformed, something beautiful to something beastly. That one same thing lost its essence. My cousin agreed, the world is a cold, cold place to be. So, Gabriel asked him, how do you save the warmth? How do you keep it? Can you? My cousin said he didn't know, that sometimes it just went away. Bled slowly out overnight. They both knew they weren't talking about fries but Gabriel was too embarrassed to point this out.

Alexandra would talk to my cousin too, not about Gabriel though, about his studies. He'd tell her what he'd been reading, Austin or McWhorter or Sapir/Whorf, and they'd argue about whether language really did shape our perception and what made things really real (stuff he and I had tired out over dinner). She told him there of course was a difference between truth and reality, that truth was more unworldly, produced. When somethings true that doesn't make it real because reality is a feeling in a way that truth isn't. It's not about what is and what isn't, but what feels. My cousin confessed that he had a small crush on her too, but he knew where he belonged.

Where's that, I asked him, taking the last bite of my burger.

Somewhere else, he said. They belonged together.

The three of them only ever saw each other at McDonalds, him sitting alone with his McNífica, them behind the counter with the machines that spin and whir in dreams, at the intersection of carnival and catastrophe. He watched them orbit, closer then further, almost touching. It made him happy, he told me, watching romance unfold in front of him.

Cómo un telenovela, un, a soap opera? Cómo se dice?

No, I know that one. Telenovela.

His smile persisted but his eyes started vibrating. He took a sip of his Dr. Pepper (the first time he had ever tried it) and kept going.

Gabriel had come up with a plan, he told him as he sat unwrapping his McNífica. To win her back, obviously. It was clear Gabriel had rehearsed this pitch. There's no one, he would tell Alexandra, no one else who he could ever... well, y'know. My cousin smiled at him. So, you're just going to confess to her? Yeah, I want to be honest. Honesty is important.

She, meanwhile, had bigger plans. Didn't harmonize with him. It was starting to get obvious, behind the counter, him sweeping, her at the register, bumping into each other, awkward, getting colder. She wanted to study linguistics like my cousin, she asked him to borrow some books. I'll bring them by next weekend.

Based on his tone I knew there was never a next weekend. As much as I knew the story, I didn't.

You ever been surprised before?

He had the article bookmarked.

They died on a Saturday night. It was probably when he was going to confess his love to her. Only probably because of that thing that happens inside you when you decide to confess your love to somebody, where you make a promise but only to yourself, and those promises are the easiest kind to break because of how they aren't really real; it's easy for you to disappoint yourself but devastating to be disappointed by someone else, especially someone you love so much. Especially when it's just the two of you, surrounded by silver machines that sound like didgeridoos. It was just the two of them, then. Graveyard shift gets its name from the men whose job it was to sit by the graveyard and listen for the frantic ringing bells of people who might have been buried alive. Probably. Restaurant nighttime is different because you usually can't see outside and so are surprised when you go out and realize the sun has set, either long before or just seconds ago. She locked the doors, the drivethru only opened. In the kitchen, when there weren't any orders they stayed on opposite ends. He'd say something across the cold aluminum countertops to her, she'd respond. This past week had felt less awkward, which was why he was probably going to confess his love to her. Is the stroke of midnight a good time to confess your love to someone? Maybe saying it in person is never a good idea. Words in the air mix things up. Some promises are broken before they're made.

There is a silent drumroll that comes with a confession of love. It's in the air, announcing the words that are going to be said. I love you, I always have, I never stopped. I could never love anybody but you. I know we don't know what's going to happen, where everything is going to go, and I know you have plans, big plans, but the only thing I know is that I love you. Still. You don't have to say anything, I just thought you should know.

What did she hear? A bunch of interfering ripples through her body. Hands tight clenching on the malfunctioning machine, standing still, nothing. He came running, to help her, like any person would. Singing through you to me, it felt closer than they had ever been before. Seeking electricity, pushing and pulling you, into something else. The lights flickered, making the whole restaurant a hospital. The double threat of illumination, dissonance, until they were both gone above themselves where you can see: God, who is small and static and everywhere moving like an infinite rise, alive and flying between taut strings, showing you the end where time and your life and everything is just a great big worm, fat and rounded like an apple pie, filled with everything you've done, all the love and grief and breath and swallows and stars, wriggling through a dark and naked vacuum. This was the only real truth—they were afraid.

"The death by electrocution of two young employees at a McDonald's restaurant in Lima has spurred protests and stoked anger over working conditions in the wider economy, which are viewed as exploitative and sometimes dangerous…

"Peru's public prosecutor's office has opened an investigation into the deaths of Alexandra Porras, 19, and her former boyfriend Gabriel Campos, 18, who were reported to have died in the early hours of Sunday while cleaning the kitchen at the fast-food outlet."

I'm sorry, I said. He took off his baseball cap for the first time all weekend. He said that he couldn't believe it, when he read it. He hadn't been able to go that weekend, he was busy writing some paper. How stupid had that been, how stupid did all papers seem, his whole degree, path, everything, if they could just die. That they could just die.

What does it mean? Sure, there's something evil in there, about corporations who don't love you, no matter how much they say they do, about never getting what you want because of how rigged everything is against you, something about being a pawn in their game. My cousin didn't talk about that, though: the only thing he knew, all

41

that he cared about and believed in was two people. Two young people. That was all that was real to him. Their faces, bones blood flesh. But if we're all as human as we say we are then it shouldn't be so hard, to love and to live. To make sure people, young people, don't die. Why do children suffer? "'Ma'am, there's been an accident,' the employee told her, she said. 'Your daughter is dead.' When she hung up, she said, she began to scream." It feels like everything is glass. Everything's a window I'm looking out of but it's all just more windows.

He dreamt about them all the next month. Several months. They were up sitting above the atmosphere, where the earth is a low jump, a sapphire lea of white and green flowers. Holding each other. Their faces more than love or fear. Saying it doesn't have to be like this.

BONE CHINA
Amaris Castillo

The first time my Abuela Elba told me she was going to die of solitude, my face was streaked with white glow-in-the-dark-paint. It was a Friday night in mid-October and I had just come home from a rave. I was 24.

My abuela lay in her twin bed a few feet from mine. The frame's metal joints cried as she turned from her side to face the ceiling. Her mahogany cheeks sagged. Her hip bones stuck out from under her favorite sky blue bata.

I inhaled sharply. My abuela looked like she was lying in repose. But this was no public viewing. Only me, her granddaughter, was subject to seeing her like this. I had convinced myself we were roommates living together in Crown Heights — a struggling artist who moonlit as a bartender and a retiree who prayed the rosary multiple times a day. And my abuela was very much alive, though for months I sensed she didn't want to be.

Jägerbombs still coated the back of my tongue as I called her name. No answer.

I tossed aside my teal shoulder purse filled with loose change and makeup. White Jesus Christ followed me from behind a smudged glass picture frame as I sat on the edge of my abuela's bed. Her eyelids striped in wrinkles twitched. I cupped her hand in mine and began to press on her palm with my fingers. She used to love when my mom gave her hand massages.

"Do you want to talk?" I asked.

She cleared her throat.

"I'm out of words," she told me in Spanish.

After a while, I gently let go. I stripped and threw on an old t-shirt and shorts. Then I walked to the bathroom to brush the alcoholic guilt off my tongue.

*

I'm told a river of blood spilled out of my abuela when she delivered her first child. She didn't name the stillbirth. When she learned her baby girl didn't make it, when she saw her reddish face and heard only piercing silence from her tiny mouth, my abuela screamed in agony. She begged the midwives to cut a few strands of her jet-black curly hair and tie it together with ribbon. My would-be tía was buried three days later, in a wooden coffin that was a bit bigger than a shoebox.

My abuela was not unlike other mothers in her mountainside town of Jarabacoa. Women losing their babies was not uncommon in the campo. Grief was the realest of chronic pains there.

And even as she held onto those strands of hair, my abuela fervently prayed for more children. She was only 19, but I'm told she wanted nothing more than to be a mother. A few years later, she and my Abuelo Leopoldo had another girl. My abuela named her Jael. I looked up the name once and it means "mountain goat." Jael was a biblical heroine who used a mallet to drive a tent peg into a man's temple.

My abuela's Jael, little Dominican Jael, grew into my mother.

*

I decided to stay home the morning after my abuela told me she was going to die of solitude for the first time. Panic lodged into my abdomen. *What does she want? Have I not done enough? What will bring her peace?* The questions played in my head, a relentless loop that drowned out the rumbling of the Franklin Avenue shuttle outside our third-floor walkup.

Sunlight teased me. It filtered into our room through lace curtains and washed over Doña Elba's sleeping face and mine. I climbed out of bed and walked barefoot to the living room. We lived in one of those railroad apartments, where you had to go through the living room to get to our room. And you had to go through our room to get to the second room at the far end of the apartment, but I never went in there. My abuela kept it secured with the assurance from a Jimmy Proof lock.

In the living room were framed photos on the wall, mostly of my mother and I. We were abuela's obsessions. In one, 19-year-old Jael carried me on her left hip at a summer block party. She wore whitewashed jeans and a magenta crop top that hugged her ribs and breasts. Her long, dark hair was pulled back tightly with gel. She looked happy holding me. I was 3 years old, dressed in a yellow romper and enjoying gofio in a soggy paper cone. I could still taste the sweet corn powder.

After studying a few more photos, I went to the kitchen to make coffee. I thought about the 15-minute walk from our place to the Central Library. My abuela had no desire to go there the last time I asked her to join me, even when I brought up the Halloween decorations we'd admire along the way. She brought up the struggle to go up and down the flights of stairs in our building. When I pointed out the reliable elevator, she still shook her head no.

In the living room I fished out a bone china teacup with gold trim from the glass display cabinet where the fancy things were kept. Picked the shiniest one for my abuela's coffee in hopes that something beautiful might uplift her. I scooped some sugar from the cupboard above the sink and prepared myself a cup next.

*

When Jael was 12, lung cancer stole her father. He was much older and had loved his cigars.

After her husband died, my abuela packed up two maletas and left for New York with her daughter. Elba Guzman, now a 30-something widow who spoke no English, found an apartment in Brooklyn, in a tenement building with a superintendent who held his immigrant tenants with disdain. She landed work at a pencil factory in Manhattan and would come home smelling like shavings. They barely scraped by, but at least young Jael always had an abundance of pencils for school.

By then it was the 1980s. I'm told crime was high in NYC, and heroin and crack fiends roamed Crown Heights in search of their next fix. Knowing Dominicans, that was most likely an exaggeration, but just two or three addicts in our hood were enough to scare my abuela into keeping her daughter locked up in their apartment.

My abuela gradually lost her grip on Jael, as if children were something to grip onto. My mother was too much of a free spirit, I'm told by people in our building, and Doña Elba was too rigid. Jael wanted to be on the stoop with the other teens whose parents let them be. She wanted to feel alive. Una andariega, according to my abuela. A girl who loves to be out and everywhere.

I'm told Doña Elba was a radiant woman but didn't know it. She made a few friends at church, but was dedicated to only God and her daughter, in that order. Before my abuela had left the Dominican

Republic, her mother had discouraged her from remarrying. My great-grandmother told her to keep Jael close.

My abuela continued to pray for her daughter, even during the stretches of days when Jael would be somewhere other than home.

One day, when she was 15, Jael told her mother she was pregnant. My abuela didn't want to believe it at first. Jael was still a child. Denial of this stubborn truth lasted about a week and, once that dissipated, Doña Elba went out and bought rosaries of all kinds – from natural stone to nylon. She wore a few on her neck, and hung the rest on a wall hook in the living room. The only time she spoke was for prayer.

From what I'm told, Jael was hurt by her mother's reaction to the news. In her rebellious spirit, she decided to stay with friends for most of the pregnancy. She convinced herself she could be a good mother. I suspect she didn't realize what that would entail until after I was born.

A few years ago, my abuela revealed more details to me about the day I came into the world. How Jael fought back tears as she handed me to her mother.

*

It was now a little past 10 a.m. My abuela was usually up by this time. Whenever I got anxiety, I would feel pangs underneath my fingernails. My hands throbbed that late Saturday morning as I brought a serving tray to our bedroom.

My abuela's bed was empty. The door to the room she kept locked was ajar. Cautiously, I slipped inside.

My eyes needed a solid minute to settle on this space I was never allowed in. The tiny room looked like it once belonged to a girl. Flecks of dust danced in the sunlight that poured in from the sole window. The walls were coated in old posters. The only one I recognized was Lisa Lisa with her dark eyeliner and big hair. There were pastel-colored scrunchies in a clear box above a dresser, and a bed to my right was neatly made.

My abuela sat on the floor clutching a green wool sweater, sobbing. Panicked, I set the tray down on the bed and joined her.

"Abuela, what's this..." I asked.

I reached over to embrace what was left of her frame. She smelled faintly of vanilla.

"Jael, she's gone," she said.

I closed my eyes and sighed.

"I know that, Abuela."

Jael had been a jumpy and sporadic presence in my life, for most of my life. Her pregnancy 25 years ago was an accident and, from what I'm told, she lacked maternal instinct. She was incapable of putting me first. Every few months she'd bring me candy and lime quarter juices from the bodega, but to actually parent me?

My mother taught me what true heartache is. I used to cry for her at night, silently so my abuela wouldn't hear. But Doña Elba always felt it. She'd nudge me and I'd climb into her bed. My abuela's love sunk deep into me. It always kept me afloat.

Did my mother even love me? The question trailed me for years. As I grew into a woman myself, I became used to her absence, clinging instead to my abuela.

Jael stopped visiting a few months ago. The last time she dropped by unannounced, she was clearly on something. Restless, she paced around the apartment and talked about how much this neighborhood had changed. She gave me an awkward hug. Her eyes lingered on the door I wasn't allowed in, but she said nothing else.

"No, mi niña bella, you don't understand," my abuela said, interrupting my thoughts. Her voice was weak.

"God has her."

What felt like a lightning bolt tore through my body. Then, soaring towards the sky.

My mother. Dead?

*

It happened in June. Jael's body was found back in an abandoned apartment in Williamsburg, in an area where Orthodox Jewish men walk in clusters and avoid eye contact with you.

The building superintendent who found Jael called the cops, who then contacted my abuela to inform her of her estranged daughter's death. A cocaine overdose.

My abuela told me she didn't know how to cope. She had already lost a daughter. And even though Jael herself walked aimlessly in life, that didn't mean that her story should end.

My abuela didn't know how to tell me. So she hid it for months until it broke her.

*

Two months went by and my abuela stopped speaking altogether. My suspicion was that her silence was rooted in grief and shame.

The shock of my mother's death had not yet waned for me, but still every morning I brought my abuela a cafecito. She'd nibble on food but could never finish the whole plate.

I knew I should remain at home with my abuela, so I told my boss at the Irish pub I work at that I needed some time off. My painting also took a pause.

In the span of an hour, I'd seesaw between disbelief and anger at my abuela for keeping the truth from me. She saved me from my mom. But then again, my mom saved me from herself.

We were in the thick of winter now, and from our living room windows I could hear perico ripiao competing with bachata from neighboring apartments. I could hear the lilt in the Dominican dialect as families yelled over music. January 1ˢᵗ was minutes away. Everyone awaited its shiny promise.

I shut the windows closed because I could no longer listen to the joy outside.

The uneven linoleum floor creaked below me as I hovered by the doorway of our bedroom. My abuela was asleep again. This time, with the aid of medication prescribed by her doctor. The orange bottle joined the others on the nightstand between our beds, below white Jesus Christ.

I knelt on the floor beside my abuela's bed and looked up at her. Her face looked beautiful under the pale light of the moon. I placed my hands on hers. She stirred awake.

"Abuela, I know you're not speaking. But I need you to hear me. I *love* you," I said softly. "You are my whole heart. It's you."

My abuela's thin lips shook a bit. She squeezed my hand. Closed her eyes again.

At the far end of our apartment is the bathroom. I locked myself in. Climbed into the clawfoot bathtub with the chipped rim and pulled my cell phone from my pocket. I wanted to dial the only number I had for my mom, to tell her what's going on with abuela. What's going on with me. It was wishful thinking that she'd answer. She's dead. Like my late abuelo, who I never had the chance to meet. I'm told he once welded two metal rocking chairs that my abuela added pillows to and together they rocked on their porch at dusk, two young lovebirds in Jarabacoa before lung cancer stole him forever. My mom is dead like my would-be tía, her tiny unfulfilled body with no name buried three days later in Dominican soil. I've been surrounded by ghosts my whole life.

My back pressed against the curve of the tub as I stretched my legs. I closed my eyes. Never had I felt this suffocated. I sank deeper until my chin dug into my sternum. My breathing grew labored, just as I'd hoped.

BORDERLAND

Sofía Aguilar

My abuela has begun laughing at Death. Brushing him off every morning from her crooked, shrunken shoulders, pinching him away from her body as resilient, as fearless as our people. Like my father dragging his mattress to the road and jumping down from the roof to touch the softness of sky and the hardness of fall, still young, still a child then. Like my tía roller skating with her sister, each with only one shoe and the crooks of their arms so braided that they weren't sure whose was whose. Like someone my abuela used to be, running before she learned to walk as though escaping her own shadow, dancing around gazebos in circles with boys and their hair as thick as a gringo's accent, their strands slicked back with gel and a comb, her shoes and her world not yet grown too small.

She cannot do this alone like she used to. Her steps so clumsy now that she once fell and cracked her rib, shattered the vase holding her heartleaf and made my tía replace the pieces with a pot. For weeks, her eyes couldn't find a way to close, her body made more of ache than bone, her slippers heel-hollowed, unfilled on the floor, her spine so bent like a lung collapsed and troubled with finding the strength to breathe. Her cries to God so loud that my tía took the room down the hall and still heard all of her voices at night as though she housed different people inside. No puedo, no puedo. Mamá, Mamá, ¿donde esta? Ay Dios Mio, estoy listo para morir, all this over and over and over again.

But still my abuela jokes every time I leave home, si todavía estoy aquí when my nieta returns, if Death doesn't steal my breath in my sleep, her life her pearled pair of aretes hidden away in the drawer like a secret or a candle aflame, a please-come-true wish. Ay, Amá, don't say such things, Mamá scolds her, my tías too, but my abuela can't hear the world right, has to have everything repeated twice as though Death stole her ears after stealing her feet, one thing at a time, yet she was the one who saw the humor in the end. Who spoke of her death as inevitable, approaching soon, like a train chugging through chain-link borderland, that rainless, faceless in between where nopales bear their fruit as though offering a sting and fear is carried in the belly like a child unborn with no brakes to stop its coming. My abuela who speaks with the mouth of an immigrant, her teeth that believe heaven and home are said the same way and stumble through inglés as though made of a thickness she cannot understand how to chew. So different from Spanish with words spoken the way they are spelled, so out of reach that she must gesture for what she's looking for, so much that the valleys of her hands ache just as well as her tongue.

My abuela who has made a fool out of Death and is only waiting to let go. I only wish I still believed in prayer or the cross above her bed to ask God for her escape. Can't hurry her out of this house even with its locks that never stay shut, even with its many doors, their width too small, too narrow, too soon to let her pass through.

LOVE LANGUAGE
Janelly Ramos

Papi Jerry would stop by and drop off groceries long after he moved out
Ñaña still calls before any trips and asks what snacks I'd like
Papi Johnny's first question is always "Do you want to eat?"
Mami drops off platanos y verengenas at my aunt's so Mama can
have her mangu for breakfast, there aren't any Latin supermarkets in
Suberbia
Sito bought me Florecitas from La Roca and I swear I cried
Mamá never fails to call me when she makes trigo
Mami drops it off along with aguacates y maduros
Even though I can easily get them
Even Sisa, who gladly refers to herself as seca and feigns disgust
when I lean in for a hug,
still saves the corner piece of the cake and extra supiro for me
This is our love language

JUANCHO LLEGA A CASA
Emerson Machtus

En ese momento, Juancho entró a su casa pensando que aun era suya. No era él una persona que fuera a olvidarse fácilmente de cómo llegar a un lugar. Especialmente si este lugar era, pues, su propia casa.

Tampoco se podría afirmar que la noche anterior hubiera dormido allí. No. Juancho sabía perfectamente como llegar hasta su puerta, pero no tenía ni puta idea de exactamente donde había pasado la noche. Se imaginaba que la ropa que llevaba puesta era suya -por lo menos le quedaba bien- y que a ciencia cierta, ni olía mal ni estaba arrugada. De hecho, Juancho estaba bastante ordenado. Afeitado al ras, pelo recién cortado, cinturón ajustado en el orificio preciso, camisa metida en el pantalón con soltura elegante, incluso se levantó el cuello de la camisa para olfatear alguna fragancia. Dulce pero sobria; aroma varonil.

Al entrar, Juancho extendió las mangas de su camisa en un movimiento acostumbrado a los gemelos. Nadie se percató de su entrada. Estaba ya en el comedor cuando una mujer joven y hermosa se cruzó con él. Juancho la reconocía como su hija, pero ella no tenía ni idea de quien era él. Intercambiaron una mirada analítica, profunda y sorprendida. El se quedó plantado allí, en el mismo lugar, inmovilizado por un acto de discernimiento voraz, que le impedía toda noción de energía física. Ella permanecía perpleja, viéndolo, oliéndolo y sintiéndose extrañamente a salvo.

Me recuerdas mucho a alguien –le dijo al extraño.

Juancho metió las manos en los bolsillos del pantalón y le respondió a su hija.

Tal vez tu también, pero no me conoces.

Siéntate allí. Te voy a poner algo –Le invitó.

Sentado en una raquítica silla, Juancho cerró los ojos cuando empezó a escuchar la música de Schoenberg. Este avasallaba cualquier resquicio de silencio en las paredes y atacaba frontalmente los párpados de Juancho. Ella subía el volumen al máximo y sonreía mientras se ponía de cuclillas. Lo estaba observando. Él estaba de frente a las bocinas. Ella se regodeaba con la exaltada emoción que le producían esas notas.

Para ellos, el tiempo fue reinventado por el silencio. La música se había terminado. Él vio que lloraba y se levantó de la silla. Le acarició la cabeza con un movimiento gentil de película en blanco y negro. Su mano temblaba.

¿Está tu madre?

Es aquella que está en el jardín —señalizaba- junto a las orquídeas.

Cualquier orquídea promedio posee una belleza que solo puede ser entendida desde el desprendimiento. Es una belleza hambrienta, que digiere, pedazo a pedazo, nuestra percepción. Juancho las conocía bien, comprendía y apreciaba la excéntrica sutileza que irradian. Se aproximó a la mujer que estaba entre las orquídeas y la cogió de la cintura. Ella volteó. El se percató de su ceguera. Inmediatamente pensó en la contradicción que suponía rodearse de todas esas formas siendo incapaz de percibirlas visualmente. Sostenía una flor rojísima en la mano y se la dio. Sonreía.

-No hace falta verlas para admirarlas. —lo sorprendió- Imagínate del poder que tengo en estos momentos. A través del tacto y el olfato puedo imaginar colores inexistentes. Alumbro la oscuridad desde la creación absoluta y distingo las profundidades de todo lo que las constituye. Ya sabes, el juego de antónimos que marca la misma existencia: sin sombra no hay luz, sin vida no hay muerte, y en este caso, sin profundidad no hay cercanía.

Juancho huele la flor que le ha otorgado.

"Me la llevaré conmigo" -Le dice emocionado.

Llevas el mismo perfume de siempre. Quiero pensar que has vuelto por algo específico.

Por esta flor, por supuesto. La estuve esperando mucho tiempo.

Pues ya la tienes.

En ese momento ella levanta su mano y la recorre por su cara. Redibuja su vitalidad, las líneas que la constituyen. Le deja un pequeño trazo de tierra en el cachete. Él cierra los ojos. Imagina el pasado. Aquellos eventos que dentro de su propia indefinición se convierten en una recreación de si mismos. El futuro imposible, la ficción real de lo sensorial. Todo el olvido cabe dentro de un solo recuerdo, y con él es posible alterar el orden del mundo. Es un viaje en el tiempo. Un mundo paralelo tan real que es comparable y confundible con el actual. Son rieles del tren. Siempre juntos pero inabarcables.

Juancho comprendió con la tersura de su piel que todo había perdido significado.

Todo es percepción –Pensó.

Todo se reduce a permanecer abierto y dispuesto a absorber el mundo que alumbra cada instante. Cada instante pluvial, envolvente.

Todo es real. Toda creación, maquinación e imaginación existe en sí misma dentro de un mundo real. Juancho entendió eso en ese momento y meditó su importancia. Le otorgó la categoría mental de Vida. Vital. Presencia real ante una posición que físicamente le era irreconocible.

Hay momentos así. Juancho lo vivió allí mismo. Su vida entera, acababa de renacer a través del tacto de una mujer a la que conocía, pero no sabía quién era. ¿Contradicción? No, congruencia. Momentos en los que todo se embuda por un cristal transparente que refleja destellos de esperanza, iluminando la muerte y marcando el camino.

Anonimato.

Juancho le devolvió la flor sin decirle nada y en sentido inverso, volvió a retomar el camino que lo trajo hasta ese jardín. Retomó su encuentro con la hermosa joven, se ensimismó de música apabullante y discerniéndola de reojo prosiguió hasta la entrada que ahora no era mas que salida. Al mismo lugar donde había llegado sin saber porqué.

Caminó y caminó por lo que parecieron meses, sin rumbo definido, siempre hacia el horizonte cercano. Marcó las distancias de la separación y sobrevivió tormentas, nevadas y hambrunas. Cruzó desiertos, atravesó exóticos campos de batalla, y navegó por ríos de cauces infinitos. Se había unido perfectamente al paisaje. Amalgamado a toda la existencia que algunos llaman Divina.

Fluir perpetuo de un organigrama desdibujado.

Mírame –Le espetó aquella mujer de cabello gris y lentes redondísimos. –Te escucho respirar. ¿No te estarás haciendo el dormido verdad? Eso aquí es muy peligroso, ¿sabes?

Juancho abría los ojos y se topaba consigo mismo, reflejado en los bifocales de la mujer que tenía directamente sobre él. Se miraba.

¿Sabes donde estas? –Le seguía preguntando.

¿Dónde estoy?

Te lo estoy preguntando. ¿Sabes donde estás?

No.

Me lo imaginaba. Ayer llegaste de noche y como si fuera tu casa, te tumbaste en aquella esquina y te quedaste de piedra por horas. Ni siquiera pestañeabas. Venías muy bien vestido, la verdad. Sabes que aquí somos todos pordioseros, muertos de hambre y borrachos. Tu apareciste engominado y oliendo a colonia fina. *Eau de toilette*, si es que me entiendes.

Te entiendo. Lo que no se es como llegué aquí.

No es la primera vez ¿sabes? Hace como unos meses se apareció por aquí un señor que vino con su chofer y todo. Habló conmigo. Muy elegante. Se sentó allí al lado de la reja y durmió aquí toda la noche y parte del día siguiente. Hablamos de todo un poco. Nada concreto. El chofer lo esperó todo el tiempo en el coche. Solo se bajó del coche para mear. La tarde siguiente se levantó, se despidió de mí y se fue. Nunca más supe de el.

Juancho la escuchaba interesado. La miraba directamente a los ojos y ella seguía, de manera muy articulada. Exageraba algunos comentarios, pero él la entendía. Vive debajo de un puente en una avenida transitada. Era lo menos que podía hacer, exagerar todo. Vivir una hipérbole.

Todo el mundo huye de algo, –Continuó- es algo que creo es inherente a nuestro instinto de supervivencia. La teoría del avestruz. Nuestra manera de esconder la cabeza es recorriendo los bordes de un problema o situación hasta que este se deforme formalmente. La distancia protectora.

¿Y tu? -Despúes de esta frase la mujer le clava la vista. Permanece en silencio un momento, viéndolo.

Juancho solo escuchaba.

¿De que huyes?

Remangándose la camisa hasta los codos, Juancho trataba de arreglarse el pelo. Un débil soplo de viento se levantaba sobre su cara.

Si te dijera que de mí mismo a lo mejor pensarías que estoy loco.

Ella espera que continúe.

Pero es cierto. Ayer me levanté para ir a trabajar como todos los días. Hacía mucho calor desde temprano y me duché con agua fría. Helada casi. Me acerqué al espejo para arreglarme el nudo de la corbata y escuché en ese instante la voz de una mujer. Me era completamente extraña. Ajena. Me observé en el espejo y casi por reflejo, tiré de la corbata, la dejé caer sobre el suelo y salí del baño. Del baño a la entrada, y de allí a la calle. Me acuerdo de poco más. En tal caso del espanto que me causó mi reflejo. Después de allí perdí noción de la distancia o de los caminos que recorría. Simplemente aparecí aquí, impulsado por alguna fuerza humana desconocida hasta ahora para mí.

La mujer permaneció callada por un momento que se extendió a través de sus miradas. Juancho empezó a llorar. La mujer lo abrazó, consolándolo.

Hiciste bien. Créeme. Lograste escapar de los brazos de la violencia.

Hubo un mutismo mas acentuado, solo interrumpido por sollozos. Juancho sabía lo que ella decía. Lo entendía muy bien. Percibió el peligro de la enajenación en aquel momento. Olió sangre. La tenía debajo de su propia nariz. Desvanecerse es lo mejor que pudo hacer.

Juancho regresaba, y mientras se acercaba volvió a levantar el cuello de su camisa. Ya no olía bien como antes. Su pelo tampoco estaba ya ordenado por la gomina. La camisa la tenía llena de marcas negras y sus uñas contenían pedazos de tierra inmunda. Le picaba el cuello y se rascaba. Las luces de la sirena policial lo guiaban de vuelta hacia su casa. Dos coches permanecían estacionados en su entrada y uno de los policías fumaba apoyado en el vehículo. Al aproximarse, el agente lo vio venir e inmediatamente fijó su mirada en él. Sacó una foto que tenía y cayó en cuenta de quien era, el desaparecido. Tiró el cigarro e hizo una llamada por su radio. Acto seguido, de la casa salió otro policía y detrás de él dos mujeres. La mayor se abalanzó sobre Juancho apretándolo con todas las fuerzas que tenía. Lloraba profusamente. La joven se quedó detrás, sonriendo, viendo a su padre mientras este abrazaba a su madre.

¿¡Dónde te metiste?! –Le recriminó la madre sin soltarlo.

Él no contestó.

Los policías se vieron entre sí y subieron a sus coches. Al doblar a la derecha, ambos apagaron sus luces.

EL CARNAVAL
Daniel Hernandez Aldaco

El colorido de las luces se dormía en brillos tenues y taciturnos, la gente se perdía a lo lejos mientras la plaza quedaba cubierta de los restos mudos y ya podridos del carnaval. Don Edmundo Ballesteros yacía recostado sobre un empedrado a la mitad del paso peatonal. Despertaba sin poder dar razón de lo que había sucedido. Mientras su visión se esclarecía alzaba la vista vislumbrando el cielo estrellado. Una, cuatro, veintiocho, mil dos, un millón veinte mil, cinco billones dos mil doscientas cuarenta y tres punto dos. No mentía, el mismo las contó una por una, había cinco billones dos mil doscientas cuarenta y tres punto dos estrellas en esa noche despejada del Lago de Guadalupe.

Ya helaba, podría jurar que la última ventisca le había congelado todo moco en su nariz y no le quedó más remedio que buscar un periódico para ponerlo debajo del abrigo y encontrar un rincón donde tomar su medicamento. "Malditas pastillas, maldito doctor, maldito frío, ya no son como antes, ya no son como antes, ya no me ponen– tal vez si tomo dos más– sí, dos más." Ya avispado se percató lo que el carnaval dejó tras de si. El pavimento yacía lleno de cubrebocas, cervezas y envolturas. Los árboles cercenados, cubiertos en papel sanitario. Una familia, con ropas tornasoladas y piel morena, rumeaba las sobras. Una joven era jaloneada por un viejo y a su lado un policía multaba borrachos. Pasmado por la escena, se vio a si mismo. Sus manos estaban ensangrentadas. Sus pies, enlodados. "¿Dónde está el piso?" exclamó asustado Edmundo. A sus pies parecía haber una costra hedionda y fétida de basura que cubría todo.

Los recuerdos de anoche le llegaban como piquetes de mosquito. De repente se entremetían imágenes de sus nietos. "Amelia…" dijo suspirando. Sacó de su billetera una foto: él cargando una bebé. Se dijo que ya pronto arreglaría todo. Recorrió el pueblo buscando la estación de tren. Anduvo por horas en círculos apenas parando para buscar agua. Cada vez le era más difícil continuar, le faltaba aire, sus piernas se acalambraban. En la plaza se sentó para reposar "el matasanos me mandó pura bala de salva" dijo mientras tomaba tres pastillas y cerraba los ojos. Despertó. Quiso reanudar, pero un crudo escalofrío le recorrió: no podía levantarse. Sus tobillos y muñecas estaban hundidas en aquella costra de basura que ya alcanzaba el medio metro.

Edmundo forcejeo aterrado, soltando efímeramente sus pies y sus brazos. "Tengo que ver a mis nietos." Fue mientras luchaba que vio que no solo era basura, eran los mismos miembros del carnaval quienes le hundían. Los árboles tirando de sus piernas, el borracho insultándole, el policía golpeándole, la mujer suplicándole, la familia limosneándole. Era un torbellino de extremidades colgándose de él, era un espiral gigante que barría el carnaval. La dialéctica de la vida y la muerte. No se rendía. "¡Yo no debo estar aquí!" Esto no le podía suceder a él, ¡Don Edmundo Ballesteros!

Pero el torbellino barría al pueblo entero de Lago de Guadalupe, a los buenos, a los malos, a los aburridos y a los septuagenarios en perpetua crisis de edad. Don Edmundo solo era el último del carnaval en reconocerse. Pronto dejó de luchar pues sabía que era imposible ir contra lo predilecto. Sintió con culposo placer que la turba lo levantaba como en sus años de conciertos. Don Edmundo Ballesteros se quitó el cubrebocas, empuñó la foto y pensó en Amelia. Volteó al cielo, miro las cinco billones dos mil doscientas cuarenta y tres punto dos estrellas y se dejó arrastrar por la turba de vida y muerte para esperar a convertirse en cenizas, y es que a final de cuentas él era polvo de estrellas y en polvo de estrellas se convertía.

THE WISDOM OF THE WOUNDED: BATTLE HYMNS FOR THE CAGED IN CORONAVIRUS TIMES

Violeta Orozco

> "Battle hymns for the broken
> Battle hymns for the misled
> Battle hymns for the wretched
> The forgotten and the dead
> Battle hymns of redemption
> Of solidarity and pride
> Battle hymns we will be singing
> At the turning of the tide."

Tom Morello

The collapse of the speculative markets of human fragility has exposed the skeleton of the machinery. The bare bones of the slave labor and the dehumanizing of others in order to humanize ourselves has brought about a state of affairs where the marginal and the liminal creatures that had been living inside the subways and the train stations have finally surfaced. The black, the brown, the homeless people, H.G Wells' Morlocks living in the underground had always been there, locked in dark alleys and underground malls, waiting for this moment of shuddering recognition. Coronavirus has allowed us to see the center of the peripheries, how all that we had tried to keep at bay by naming it, relegating it to another planet, a different species or a different race, was part of this world. The rabble. The people we had construed as zombies coming out of their grave to touch us and infect us were uncannily similar to the mob of homeless people in Penn station approaching strangers to demand change. How wrong we were. The enemy is human, and the enemy is within. It did not come from another planet to invade our world. We are the world that wanted to keep the menace of the other in a cage, without realizing we were the other.

We were the tourists that wanted to do the slum tour without the risk, the landfill tour without the stench, to watch the war through a screen so it would not hurt us, so we could render it unreal. And now that dead people are piling in the parks and even the founders of funeral homes are dying, we start to remember Hamlet's gravediggers' dialogues. The blazing unreality of the gravediggers digging their own graves is as unlikely as the tale of the bodies that would not fit in all the frozen trailers in New York. The homeless people populating the subway, the sub world that they had finally reclaimed.

For a few days, it seemed that with the confinement, the abused and the mentally unstable, the bullied and the battered were surfacing from the underworld we had locked them in, terrified of their uncanny stories. Fiona Apple released her new album, and the broken girl I had been, seeking solace in songs of misfit suburban girls realized the wisdom of the wounded was finally starting to be acknowledged. We had been nothing but a social experiment, our index of social resilience had been tested to the limit. Our pain had been transformed into battle hymns for the broken, the wretched, the forgotten and the dead as Tom Morello sang. Now it was their turn to feel caged, the turn of those who had caged us: the avid and curious little girls who had craved to go out and explore a misogynistic world.

Like the characters in Alma Villanueva's Weeping woman: La Llorona and other stories, the girls in my home state in the peripheries of Mexico City had grown among stories of rape, kidnapping and women's murders. But this had never been labeled gender violence, this had been our daily bread. We had been taught never to go out on our own.

The girls in the infamous city of Ecatepec in the State of Mexico could not even go to the convenience store or the butcher for peril of getting butchered in front of their house. It was common for women to appear in garbage bags and dumps and rivers in their own neighborhood years before the term femicide had a wide press in Mexico. But nobody said anything, they were all terrified into silence. And wasn't this what they got for being poor, the lot they had been assigned for being women? Calling the police was useless, why, if even their girls disappeared in front of police stations, police were well known to be rapists and burglars, rendered invulnerable because of their privileged relationship with the law. I remember how my dad had forbidden me to walk in front of the police station a block away from my house since elementary school, even when my elementary school was right next to the police station. He would always pick me up in his motorcycle, too terrified to let me walk the 50 feet that separated me from my house as a child. I became a cyclist and a soccer player, the only way to escape my half mile radius. I was a prisoner with a library and a piano, trapped in the isolated suburbs of Mexico City, my instruments for an isolated freedom.

My isolation now reminds me of those times. The strange loneliness of the suburbs. The impotence of my isolation, the subdued scream of my body caged in a house where I was condemned to stay like a sieged town. A silent spring, with cars parked in front of every building, ambulances being the only sound disturbing the imaginary peace of the strange silence of the suburbs. And now the siege was real. Curfew, a word I thought I would never use, a word reserved to books of bygone ages and forgotten customs like war and plague. All the stories of plague famine slowly leaking through my wounded memory: the pied piper of Hamelin, Knut Hamsun's Hunger, Camus' La peste and my persistent craving for warm human bodies. Bizarre landscapes of perplexed trees, the rustle of leaves or voices in the rarefied air, the unsettling atmosphere of a threatened town. A lonely spring, an incomplete flowering. My memories simmering in the broken landscape, as if the absence added another dimension to space.

I think of all the people that were already confined. I think of the nursing homes in New Jersey, hiding the bodies and the numbers, piling them one on top of each other, refusing to confess how little the old mattered for the state. Only two years ago we had gone caroling for all the nursing homes in the little city of Athens, Ohio, for Christmas eve. The children's choir, the pianist and I would tiptoe into the hallways and the common areas, suddenly bursting into song in the dining halls, surprising the seniors in the middle of their activities. More than joy, their faces showed surprise at our presence, as if unaccustomed to visitors other than their families. A very old and thin lady crept next to an abstracted Laura on the piano, and stopped the music abruptly, towering over the piano. The pianist looked up, alarmed at the lady, who announced in a thundering voice full of rancor "I am going to die" seconds after dropping next to the piano in the middle of the room. That image has stayed with me for many winters, as if her utterance had been a threat more than a warning, as if me and Laura owed her something and she wanted, with one terrible pouncing sentence, to get it back all at once. I cannot help thinking of her, of the trembling fury in her tone as I read of the thousands of deaths of people in nursing homes across the United States. It was not just the anger in her voice that scared us. It was the definitive, irrefutable tone in which she said it, adding the final dramatic words "and I am alone" before fainting. One year later, I finally understood why she came to us, two young foreign strangers in the nursing home. It was an act of protest of the way in which she was going to die, isolated and anonymous, barely a number in the state-count chart.

The collapse of the speculative markets of human fragility has exposed the skeleton of the machinery. Economic fragility has rendered us vulnerable to exploitation. And exploitation rendered us vulnerable to dehumanization. Or rather, we were already used to being slowly dehumanized. For all those of us who came from big cities with no room in them, we had already abstracted ourselves as quantities, bodies occupying space. Those of us who were used to being women, migrants, ethnic minorities, people of color, latinx, low-paid workers, senior citizens, poor students, unemployed graduates, the great big rabble of human misery deemed expendable, there had never been any room, the table had always been full and we had never been invited. We had already been caged by our poverty, the color of our skin, our country of origin or destination. The virus was just a magnifying glass. But maybe this magnifying glass will help those who never had any freedom to refuse to have their futures foreclosed until further notice. Perhaps, like that old, indignant lady, we will finally stand up and let the orchestra directors know that we refuse to die, we refuse to be discarded.

DIARIO DE UN VIRUS
Adlyz Caliman

I – Antes de la cuarentena

¿Que porqué escribo sobre el Coronavirus? No tengo otra opción. Esta pandemia mundial ha absorbido todo mi mundo, toda mi realidad, parece que vivo en una película de ciencia ficción que me ha atrapado.

Siento que pronto mi vida será publicada y todos podrán ver mis intimidades encerrada en mi casa, al mejor estilo de Jim Carrey en El Show de Truman.

Y en verdad no escribo sobre el Coronavirus, no soy médico y no es mi intención dar estadísticas ni recomendaciones al respecto, sólo quiero compartir mi experiencia desde el encierro.

Los primeros días que supe del COVID-19 lo veía muy lejos. Una población China que se infectó porque alguien decidió comerse un murciélago enfermo (otro tema a discutir es la veracidad o no de esta afirmación). En este continente una epidemia se veía surreal.

Solo un mes después, el virus se expandía por Europa y comencé a ver la situación más en detalle, sin embargo, todavía no sentía que fuera un problema mundial, mucho menos mío.

II – Primer día de la cuarentena

Y entonces me llegó el momento, la pandemia me aplastó como se aplasta una cucaracha. La cantidad de información que veía y leía me saturó, como el virus te satura las células. A ratos sentía los síntomas, a ratos pensaba que haríamos para que esta enfermedad no acabara con la humanidad.

Ya no pensaba en mí, pensaba en mis padres, mis tías, mis suegros, mis familiares que pertenecían al grupo de alto riesgo, y decidí quedarme en mi casa; no para no enfermarme, sino para no contagiarlos.

Actos de solidaridad y de conciencia familiar y ciudadana se multiplicaron por el mundo. La vocación médica y de sanidad en general, era aplaudida y sus ejecutores los nuevos héroes con guantes y mascarillas de este desastre epidemiológico mundial.

De pronto, en el medio del cerco de la cuarentena, ya no podía visitar a mis padres, a mis familiares de mayor edad. Les llevaba la compra de comida para que ellos no tuvieran que salir, pero no podía besarlos ni abrazarlos, y algo tan cotidiano como el saludo, se convirtió en un imposible que deseaba con todas mis fuerzas.

III – Séptimo día de cuarentena

Una avalancha de videos, cadenas de whats app, audios, twitter, instagram, tik toks, me abrumaban a diario. Mi entretenimiento más agradable –leer- pasó a un segundo plano. No podía concentrarme en leer un libro, ni siquiera en ver una película, toda mi atención estaba dirigida a la información –verdadera o falsa- del COVID19.

Y entonces, después de una semana de confinamiento, fue que me comencé a relajar, sólo para volverme a preocupar cuando empecé a pensar en el más allá. ¿Hasta cuándo duraría el confinamiento? ¿Un mes? ¿Dos meses? La vacuna no estaría lista hasta dentro de un año –con suerte-. No podemos ni física, ni económica ni emocionalmente estar un año o más encerrados. ¿Y entonces? ¿Qué haríamos? ¿Entregarnos como Abraham entregó a su hijo a Dios? ¿Esperar el contagio así nada más?

Y entendí que este virus se mueve como las olas, sube y baja y debíamos estar preparados para ello.

Los gobiernos deben tomar sus medidas preventivas para evitar que suban los picos de infección mientras no exista la vacuna.

Nosotros debemos aprender a vivir con el miedo de infectar a nuestros seres queridos pero mejor aún, a vivir con la solidaridad por delante, con el pensamiento centrado en el otro y no en uno mismo.

Eso nos va a salvar de esta pandemia, la certeza de la otredad. Somos seres culturales, unidos por el sentimiento de solidaridad y la protección del clan. Eso que hizo que el hombre de las cavernas se multiplicara y perdurara en la tierra para poblarla, nos permitirá seguir unos cuantos millones de años más en la tierra… claro, si el próximo meteorito nos lo permite…

IV – Décimo quinto día de cuarentena

Subí a la azotea del edificio donde vivo a hacer algo de ejercicio y mover los músculos de mi cuerpo que me pedían estiramiento más allá de un par de metros sin conseguir alguna pieza de mobiliario.

Puedo ver el 70% de la ciudad desde mi ubicación en la azotea y la ausencia de tráfico es aterradora. Si ya veía solitaria la ciudad desde mi piso, desde el último, podía ver la extensión del acatamiento de la medida de confinamiento. Hasta los pájaros se sometían voluntariamente al retiro de los aires de la ciudad.

Parecía que un domo de algún material invisible se hubiera apostado sobre la ciudad y la mantuviera aislada de cualquier sonido. El silencio y la ausencia, me pinchaban el estómago y mi conciencia me decía : *mira Adlyz, así luce una ciudad abandonada.*

Agradecí que el ejercicio me subió las endorfinas y una llamada en grupo de mis familiares en el exterior, disiparon el sentimiento de soledad que se había instalado en mis entrañas.

V – Trigésimo día de cuarentena

No sé como ha pasado tanto tiempo.

Me prometí escribir al menos cada semana y de repente pasaron 20 días.

Y así pasa la vida. Un día pensamos que seremos el mejor escritor del mundo y al otro, han pasado 20 años y no hemos escrito nada.

¿Pero sabes qué? La vida sigue. El tiempo sigue contando su paso inexorable mientras nos lamentamos y nos quejamos. Pero también hacemos y triunfamos. Y si hace 20 años nos propusimos algo que no cumplimos, en su lugar hicimos alguna otra cosa que rindió sus frutos y valió la pena. Lo importante es no dejarnos vencer por el miedo, la inactividad y la dejadez. Que la acción domine nuestra vida. ¿Y porqué no? Empezar a cumplir el sueño que tenemos desde hace tiempo .

Quizás tenga hijos durante esta cuarentena que ya va para sesentena.

Un libro es un hijo.

¿y tú? ¿Ya te decidiste?

VI– 365 días de cuarentena

En el apartado III de este mini diario de un virus, escribí que no podíamos estar un año encerrados, y efectivamente así ha sido.

Progresivamente salimos a reencontrarnos, a mirarnos a las caras (sin vernos los dientes ni los labios), aprendimos a sonreír con la mirada, a limpiarnos las manos cada vez que teníamos contacto con algo ajeno, a mantener una distancia prudente con los demás, a trabajar y arriesgarnos a atrapar el virus con el temor de morir en el intento.

Y así como la humanidad ha sobrevivido durante todas las guerras y pandemias de su historia, sobreviviremos a esta y a las que estén por venir.

Esta cuarentena que lleva un año entre encierros y libertades, ha provocado un profundo cambio en mi vida en todos los aspectos: sentimental, laboral y migratorio. Me ha puesto a reflexionar sobre la levedad de la vida, sobre el descubrimiento de mis propias posibilidades y el efecto que mis decisiones pueden causar en mi y en las personas que me rodean, la necesidad de un abrazo caluroso, de una llamada afectuosa.

Este año ha estado lleno de tristezas y sinsabores, pero también de alegrías, esfuerzos y sobre todo, de búsqueda personal en la que me pierdo con frecuencia entre las intermitencias del amor, el desamor y el deseo.

Es por ello que no puedo juzgar al COVID con desprecio, ya que me ha obligado a poner en perspectiva muchas cosas que antes daba por ciertas y naturales, y me ha empujado a tomar decisiones y asumir riesgos, que no hubiera elegido en otra situación de "control".

Aún continuamos en pandemia, y aunque la vacuna va llegando con su dosis de esperanza, las secuelas de este virus quedarán impregnadas en mi vida para siempre.

¿Y a ti? ¿Te dejó secuelas el Coronavirus?

EL CUERPO
Yubany Checo

Puse la emisora para escuchar la meditación. Últimamente era la única forma con la que conseguía relajarme. Me pidió imaginara mi cuerpo como una cremallera que abría de arriba hasta abajo. Inhalé, cerré los ojos, exhalé más despacio. Saqué mis piernas de las piernas, mis brazos de los brazos, mi cabeza de la cabeza y dejé mi cuerpo tirado sobre el asiento como si fuera una ropa vieja. Caminé por un prado lleno de rosas amarillas y sentí mi cuerpo ligero hasta que unos golpecitos me interrumpieron. Abrí los ojos y ante mi apareció un hombre. Tenía su rostro pegado al cristal de mi puerta, se le iluminaba con las luces del camión que venía de reversa.

—Debe moverse —me dijo —viene el camión de la basura.

El reloj de carro me advirtió faltaba poco para mi cita.
—Gracias, ya lo haré —le respondí.

Mientras conducía hasta la esquina del hospital, recordé a mis tíos. Por ellos estaba aquí. Además, a mi edad era necesario practicarme el estudio. Así lo sugirió el único que quedada de ellos. Lo recuerdo esa tarde en la que la gente pasaba cerca de nosotros con los vasitos de café en las manos. Hablábamos del penúltimo fallecido.

—Parece que nos vamos muriendo por turnos —   afirmó con voz resignada.
Pensé que lo que decía era una exageración pero las evidencias eran contundentes: el abuelo, mi padre, mis tíos, todos habían muerto de lo mismo.

—Vaya al médico sobrino, todo con tiempo tiene solución—acentuó frunciendo los labios. Luego se   llevó un cigarrillo a la boca y pasó el resto de esa tarde   apagándolos con las puntas de sus zapatos.

A diferencia de mis tíos, nunca me enfermé. Mis visitas al hospital fueron para acompañar a mi padre. De niño, mamá me cuidó con esmero: gel anti bacterias, cloro para lavar las verduras, vitaminas, aseo de las manos al punto que en esa época solo contraje catarros fuertes. De un tiempo para acá corro tres veces a la semana y la presión arterial se mantiene en doce-setenta. No fumo ni como frituras. La sal y azúcar están controladas al igual que el alcohol que se reduce a beber dos copas de vino con Graciela y solo los fines de semana.

De camino al consultorio no dejé de pensar en lo frágil y desconocido que es nuestro cuerpo. Es una especie de caja que para saber su funcionamiento debemos recurrir a tubos, extracción de fluidos, tactos y cámaras.

Primero fue la sonografía que hizo una mujer a la que seguí por un pasillo angosto. Duré casi una hora acostado en una camilla mientras me pasaba una paleta untada de gel por el vientre. Noté que lo disfrutaba.

—¿Porque le indican el estudio?

—Antecedentes familiares—respondí.

Ella miraba detenidamente mis órganos que como manchas oscuras aparecían a través de su monitor.

—¿Lo han operado alguna vez?

—Nunca—le dije.

—Debo confirmar algo.

Presionó la espátula más fuerte contra mi vientre al punto de molestarme. Escuché sus dedos digitar sobre el teclado. Hizo una pausa, se levantó y salió de la habitación.

—Espere un momento—me pidió.

La escuché hablar con alguien en el pasillo. Asomó la cabeza y me miró con ojos tiernos. Alargó su mano para pasarme un poco de papel.

—Límpiese, hemos terminado.

Quise preguntarle si había visto algo anormal en mi interior aunque al hacerlo ponía en duda lo bien que funcionaba mi cuerpo. Me contuve.

—¡Adiós! —le dije.

—¡Suerte! —me respondió.

Hubiese querido dijera «todo en orden, o no se preocupe, usted está sano».

Luego vino la toma de muestras, un proceso más sencillo. De todas formas, lo considero un desperdicio por llenar tantos tubos de sangre.

—Mañana a las tres de la tarde estarán listos—confirmó la bio analista.

—Los necesito para hoy—le reclamé.

—Mañana a las tres de la tarde ¿me escuchó?

Su voz no se correspondía con la sonrisa que me daba y viendo que no llegaríamos a ningún acuerdo, terminé aceptando mañana a las tres.

Esa tarde, después del entierro de mi último tío, llegué a casa sin ganas de hablar. La voz de Graciela era un murmullo lejano. Comentó sobre lo fácil que estaba el tránsito en la ciudad, las clases virtuales, las vacunas, el encierro. Todo era un esfuerzo por invitarme a conversar pero yo le daba respuestas cortas hasta que se cansó de proponerme temas y se fue al baño. Entonces aproveché para avanzar con los reportes de mis clientes. Encendí la portátil y al instante un mensaje apareció en la pantalla: *"presione el botón si quiere conocer su carta astral".*

Nunca creí que los astros, tan distantes, tuvieran algo que ver con la salud de las personas. Estaba seguro que mis decisiones eran actos libres de su influencia. Cerré el mensaje pero minutos después reapareció. Decía lo mismo aunque ahora mostraba una serie de signos que luego descubrí eran los del zodiaco.

La secretaria del consultorio me pidió el seguro médico.

—¿Es la primera vez que viene?

—No, la segunda. Traigo los resultados —le dije levantando el sobre para que lo viera.

—Son dos mil pesos. Usted es el siguiente tan pronto se abra la puerta.

Me senté frente a ella. Giraba el sobre entre mis dedos, quería abrirlo. Al fin de cuentas, la información era mía y tenía derecho a saberla, pensé. Recordaba que los de mi padre siempre tenían una línea que decía: «positivo». Por eso, al desdoblar las páginas busqué esa nota pero no la vi. En su lugar encontré números. Confié podía hallar la explicación en Internet y así fue.

Tome los dos números y divida el primero entre el segundo. El cociente que resulte debe ser menor a uno. Si es mayor entonces su diagnóstico es positivo.

Parecía más sencillo que los cálculos en los reportes de mis clientes. Sin embargo, después de releer las instrucciones y repetir la operación, el resultado dio mayor. A pesar del frio que salía del aire acondicionado, las manos me sudaron. Quizás Internet estaba equivocada, me dije. Levanté la cabeza y miré alrededor. Había cerca de mí un grupo hombres viejos, con ojeras y caras de mal presagio. Pensé en los años junto a Graciela, en los ahorros de nuestra vejez y ahora debía agregar a la lista mi plan funerario.

Soy de los que digo que si nuestro cerebelo estuviera siempre activo, el cuerpo sería más amigable. Tal vez pudiera avisarnos con tiempo cuando el azúcar en la sangre o la presión arterial suban o bajen; sobre los tumores que pudieran aparecer en algún rincón de nuestros intestinos, en fin, hacer algo parecido a mi laptop cuando se va quedando sin carga. Pero no era ni seria así. Mi cuerpo como el de los demás usaba el dolor para avisarnos cuando algo andaba mal.

El teléfono vibró dentro de mi pantalón. Confirmé era el mismo mensaje aunque ahora me pedía mi fecha y hora de nacimiento. El último dato no lo sabía y por eso me lo inventé. Cuando llené las preguntas, la pantalla cambió de color: «estamos procesando su carta astral». En segundos apareció. Tuve la sensación de estar frente a un viejo documento lleno de símbolos y números que no comprendía. Algunas líneas de texto trataban de explicarme lo que significaba cada cosa. Por un instante olvidé los resultados y me concentré en la carta astral, en especial lo que decía en estas líneas:

Con el Sol o la Luna en Escorpio debe prestar atención a cualquier trastorno genito-urinario.

Me espanté cuando la secretaria pronunció mi nombre.

—Señor, señor es su turno —repitió.

Me incorporé como tirado por una fuerza superior pero ya no importaba escuchar lo que el doctor tenía que decirme. La ciencia y lo místico habían coincidido, se le habían adelantado en el diagnóstico. La pequeña glándula tenía todas las de ganar, yo sería el próximo en lista de la familia.

Desde el umbral de la puerta, la mirada se me extendió hasta el fondo y se detuvo justo en el escritorio del doctor. Todavía conservaba su piel salpicada de lunares y la voz que parecía resonarle en el vientre.

—¿Que lo trae por aquí?

—Vine por los resultados.

Me hizo las mismas preguntas que le hacía a mi papá. Yo respondía con la voz cortada, ahora poseída por un temblor que me hizo carraspear.

El doctor revisó la sonografía, las analíticas. Tomaba algunas notas y asentía.

Entonces levantó la cabeza y puso su mirada en mí. El temblor de mi voz pasó a mis piernas. Apreté las manos. Por primera vez me fijé en los objetos que adornaban el consultorio. A mi derecha estaba la foto de un pene y sus testículos diseccionados. Los certificados de cursos y cuadros familiares colgaban en la pared del frente. En su escritorio había un pequeño cráneo por cuyas cuencas salía la cabeza y cola de una serpiente.

—Todo luce bien. —

Quería preguntarle si estaba completamente seguro de lo que decía.

—Venga, sígame —dijo

—Bájese los pantalones, coloque los codos sobre la camilla.

Esta es la única forma de llegar hasta donde está la pequeña. Así la llamó.

Escuché cuando se puso los guantes de látex. Se untó el dedo mayor de crema y sin demoras lo entró y lo hizo girar como si describiera un círculo perfecto. El silencio llenó el lugar.

—Todo está bien con usted.

—¿Cómo dijo? —reaccioné exaltado como si quisiera escuchar lo contrario.

—Usted es un hombre sano pero la ciencia nos pide estar seguros

Traté de respirar pausado. Pronuncié una oración que aprendí de mamá. Pensé en papá y en mis tíos pero también en los resultados, en la carta astral.

—Venga en seis meses —me pareció fue lo que dijo   el doctor pero ahora no estoy seguro o tal vez lo   inventé.

La meditación hacía eco en mi cabeza: lo que piensas define lo que eres... hoy aprenderemos a vivir un día a la vez... Salí cuando el camión de basura se había ido.

SOÑANDO DESPIERTA

Graciela Matrajt

Esa mañana tenía que ir al laboratorio a recoger los resultados de unos análisis. El día estaba fresco pero soleado e invitaba a caminar. Así que en vez de ir en bicicleta como solía hacerlo, preferí caminar un poco sobre el malecón y bordear el agua. Me habían dicho que los resultados no estarían listos antes de las 2:30 y eran las 11:40, así que tenía tiempo para caminar. En el trayecto, que conocía de memoria porque era también la ruta hacia mi trabajo, me topé con un café que no había notado antes, quizás porque pasaba rápido con mi bicicleta y no había prestado atención. El olor a café me invitó a entrar y cuando estuve dentro fui a la terraza para disfrutar del sol. Allí encontré una mesa libre y apenas me hube instalado el mesero se acercó a tomar la orden. "Un capuchino", pedí. Mientras me quitaba el abrigo empecé a observar las otras mesas y la gente que las ocupaba. Tuve suerte de encontrar esta, ya que todas las demás parecían ocupadas. Observé que en la mayoría de ellas había una sola persona sentada. Solamente en dos de las otras mesas había más de una persona: en una había una pareja tomada de la mano; en la otra había un grupo de tres, estudiantes quizás, que conversaban y reían sin disimulo.

La gente solitaria de las otras mesas parecía absorta en algún objeto tecnológico. Algunos escribían en sus laptops con tal fuerza y concentración que el sonido del teclado casi opacaba las carcajadas ruidosas del grupo de estudiantes. Los otros tenían los ojos fijos en sus teléfonos y sus dedos, los más rápidos del oeste, se movían a la velocidad de la luz componiendo textos y deslizando pantallas.

Nunca me han gustado estos artefactos tecnológicos. Si bien reconozco que es práctico enviar un texto o consultar el internet desde virtualmente cualquier rincón del mundo, sea un café, una sala de espera, una parada de autobús o un taxi, siento que el contacto humano, así como la comunicación y el lenguaje que tanto nos caracterizan como especie y nos distinguen de los otros animales, se ha venido perdiendo entre la enorme cantidad de gigabytes que nos rodea. Y aunque, como el resto del mundo, yo también tengo un teléfono "inteligente", prefiero la inteligencia de los libros y siempre cargo uno en mi bolso, que saco y leo en ocasiones como esta. Porque leer bajo el sol acompañada de un buen cafecito es un placer insuperable que se da rara vez, sobre todo en una ciudad donde las nubes son a menudo las maestras de ceremonias. Así que, instalándome en la mesa, saqué el libro que estaba leyendo (*Ciudad de cristal*, de Paul Auster), me acomodé plácidamente frente al sol a saborear mi capuchino y me sumergí en mi lectura.

Después de un rato tuve la sensación de que alguien me observaba. Levanté discretamente los ojos mientras seguía sosteniendo el libro abierto y moviendo ligeramente la cabeza, como un periscopio, miré delante de mí, a la derecha y a la izquierda. Nada. Los solitarios en las mesas a mi alrededor estaban demasiado ocupados manipulando sus celulares o torturando el teclado de sus computadoras. Los que estaban acompañados seguían felices en sus conversaciones y probablemente ni siquiera me notaron cuando me senté en esta mesa. Tratando de no caer en la paranoia, evité mirar detrás de mí, en parte porque creía recordar que solo había dos mesas detrás, ocupadas por la pareja y el grupo de estudiantes, y en parte porque ya para entonces había dejado de importarme. Estaba demasiado entretenida en mi libro y quería volver a mi lectura cuanto antes.

Seguí leyendo por casi una hora. Mis párpados empezaron a pesarme y comencé a sentirme como sonámbula. Dejando el libro, todavía abierto, sobre la mesa hice una pausa y en ese momento percibí un olor mentolado, más específicamente de té de menta, que venía de algún lugar cercano. Ahora el olor se alejaba y entendí que era el mesero quien, trasladando en su charola la bebida, llevaba el delicioso aroma a otra parte de la terraza. Me encanta el té de menta y, a juzgar por el perfume tan penetrante, evidentemente este té estaba hecho con menta muy fresca. Pensé "si hubiese sabido me habría pedido uno", pero aún con el gusto de mi capuchino en el paladar volví a tomar mi libro y seguí leyendo un rato más.

Finalmente, llegué a un punto en mi lectura que me invitaba a cerrar y dejar el libro y simplemente reflexionar un rato sobre lo que acababa de leer. No hay nada más agradable que tomarse su tiempo para digerir con calma lo que uno está leyendo. Miré la hora y vi que todavía tenía tiempo de sobra. Decidí que iría a caminar un rato y contemplar el agua, así que pedí la cuenta. Cuando el mesero vino le pregunté por el té de menta: "¿Lo hacen con menta fresca, verdad?". "Trataré de recordarlo la próxima vez que venga por aquí", agregué.

Mientras esperaba a que el mesero me trajera el cambio, cerré los ojos y alcé la cara para que el sol me diera directamente. Qué sensación tan agradable era el roce de esos rayos en mi rostro a la vez que un suave viento, la brisa del canal, soplaba e invadía la terraza.

Esta sensación fue interrumpida por el mesero quien, dejando el cambio sobre la mesa, también posó un vaso transparente con té de menta diciéndome "este té se lo manda el señor", apuntando con su índice a una mesa a mi izquierda que antes no había visto. "¿Qué señor?" pregunté, al tiempo que volteaba hacia esa dirección. El mesero señaló con la mirada hacia una mesa donde había un hombre de pelo negro y ondulado y una barba también negra y densa, quien, al cruzar miradas, levantó tímidamente la mano para saludarme. Cuando el mesero se disponía a irse, yo lo detuve y, sacando una pluma de mi bolso y usando un pedazo de mi servilleta, escribí "gracias". Después de doblarla en dos se la entregué al mesero pidiéndole que se la llevara a mi generoso espía.

Un minuto después este se acercó y, preguntándome si me gustaba el té, me pidió sentarse. Yo accedí.

Mi invitado me dijo que había notado que yo estaba leyendo un libro de Auster, que era su autor predilecto. Y que también se había percatado de que el libro estaba en un idioma distinto al suyo y al del lugar donde nos encontrábamos, exponiendo así mi condición de extranjera.

Por un rato hablamos del libro y de mis dos países de origen, Argentina y México. De ahí siguió una serie de preguntas relacionadas con mi presencia en este país extranjero, mi acento al hablar esa lengua, también extranjera, y mi interés por este autor. También hablamos de poesía, de poetas latinoamericanos, de Benedetti, mi poeta favorito, y de cine. Mi curioso interlocutor me confesó que era actor y que a él también le gustaba mucho el cine. Y que alguna vez había visitado el cono sur. Su voz de barítono era suave y tenue. Nunca había escuchado una voz tan delicada en un hombre. Era como si cada palabra pronunciada transmitiera calma, como una canción de cuna. Mientras me relataba su viaje a Sudamérica, empecé a contemplar sus facciones. Empezando por su pelo ondulado y grueso, me detuve en sus ojos, negros y grandes y profundamente expresivos. Cejas pobladas. ¿Ojos típicos del medio oriente? Quizás. Seguí detallándolo y esta vez me detuve en su boca, casi por accidente. Él comentó algo gracioso y fue su sonrisa, simple pero carismática, la que llamó mi atención. Enmarcada en una barba oscura y abundante que descendía hasta su prominente manzana de Adán, mostraba una tímida cicatriz en el labio superior, camuflada por un denso bigote igualmente oscuro. Al bajar la mirada para asir mi té tropecé con sus manos grandes que, apoyadas sobre la mesa, sostenían mi servilleta doblada entre sus dedos afilados, ligeramente cubiertos de discretos vellos.

Después de un rato de charla amena hubo un silencio, de esos en los que los interlocutores aprovechan para estudiar al otro, reflexionar en algunas de las frases intercambiadas y planear lo siguiente que queremos expresar. Una pausa necesaria para iniciar una nueva conversación, la que va a determinar si habrá otras en el futuro, o si es un simple diálogo de cortesía que anuncia el inminente punto y aparte. Sin embargo, durante ese silencio, sus ojos con esa mirada penetrante seguían hablando y, como una segunda voz, me suplicaban que esto no fuera el epílogo, sino el prólogo de una historia, nuestra historia, la que acabábamos de empezar.

El capuchino, y ahora también el té, habían hecho camino hasta mi vejiga. Hacía ya un rato que me pedían a gritos libertad. Así que aproveché este silencio para levantarme y, diciéndole a mi nuevo amigo "ahora vuelvo", me dirigí al baño.

Cuando salí, unos minutos más tarde, eché un vistazo a mi mesa y descubrí con sorpresa que estaba vacía. Mi espía no estaba sentado ni en mi mesa ni en la que fue la suya. Escudriñé alrededor, deteniéndome en cada una. Después fui al interior del local imaginando que quizás se había movido hacia allí, cerca del baño, y me estaba esperando. Pero no había nadie, toda la clientela parecía estar en la terraza. Volví a mi mesa y, recogiendo mi bolso, noté la servilleta sobre el mantel. Seguía plegada. Al abrirla noté que no había nada escrito en ella. Sobre la mesa quedaba la taza de lo que había sido mi capuchino, pero no había traza del vaso que había contenido mi té.

Levantando la mirada, aceché una vez más la presencia de mi espía con la esperanza de que todo esto no hubiese sido solo un sueño. Después me fijé en la hora. Mi reloj marcaba las 2:20. Echando un último vistazo, salí del café y emprendí la marcha hacia el laboratorio.

TRENZARÉ MI TRISTEZA
Paola Klug

Decía mi abuela que cuando una mujer se sintiera triste lo mejor que podía hacer era trenzarse el cabello; de esta manera el dolor quedaría atrapado entre los cabellos y no podría llegar hasta el resto del cuerpo. Había que tener cuidado de que la tristeza no se metiera en los ojos pues los haría llover; tampoco era bueno dejarla entrar en nuestros labios pues los obligaría a decir cosas que no eran ciertas; que no se meta entre tus manos—me decía— porque puedes tostar de más el café o dejar cruda la masa, y es que a la tristeza le gusta el sabor amargo. Cuando te sientas triste niña, trénzate el cabello; atrapa el dolor en la madeja y déjalo escapar cuando el viento del norte pegue con fuerza.

Nuestro cabello es una red capaz de atraparlo todo, es fuerte como las raíces del ahuehuete y suave como la espuma del atole.

Que no te agarre desprevenida la melancolía mi niña, aun si tienes el corazón roto o los huesos fríos por alguna ausencia. No la dejes meterse en ti con tu cabello suelto, porque fluirá en cascada por los canales que la luna ha trazado entre tu cuerpo. Trenza tu tristeza, decía, siempre trenza tu tristeza…

Y mañana que despiertes con el canto del gorrión la encontrarás pálida y desvanecida entre el telar de tu cabello.

ABOUT THE AUTHORS

Aleyda Cervantes, or Mari for her familia, is a self-identified third world woman, who grew up in a small town of Guadalajara, Mexico. She attended Western Washington University where she graduated from Fairhaven College with an Interdisciplinary major titled "Solidarity Across borders: Understanding Experiences and Imagining New Realities through Storytelling" and a minor in Education and Social Justice. She is a TEDx presenter and her research around transnational feminist literature has been presented in various conferences. Collectively, she wrote the chapter, "The Demand: Pasts, Present, and Future of Black, Indigenous, and Queer of Colour Feminism," which appeared on the anthology Gendering Globalization, Globalizing Gender: Postcolonial Persepctives Edited by Gül Çalışkan. She currently works at College building bridges between underrepresented students and the world of higher education. She also makes the time to write and dream a little more in occupied Coast Salish territory.

Mayté Castro is a writer and educator currently residing in Seattle, WA. Mayte's poetry showcases the existence of what is means to be bilingual and bi-cultural while navigating these worlds within the United States of America. Mayte is a daughter of Mexican immigrants and identifies as Latine.

Ramon Jimenez is a writer and educator who resides in Seattle, WA. He teaches language arts and runs a summer youth poetry program. He writes poetry that focuses on immigration, culture and travel. He is interested in exploring locations and how they connect to memories. His poems are published in Rigorous Magazine and the Anti-Languorous Project.

Dulce Mata is a first-year graduate student pursuing a Masters in Spanish with a concentration in Creative Writing at The University of Texas Rio Grande Valley. She is originally from Coahuila, Mexico and immigrated to the United States at the age of five. She enjoys reading and writing; her poetry in English and Spanish explores themes of self-reflection, immigration and social injustices.

Hannah Martinez is a student studying history in New England. She has written poetry before and was published in the fifth issue of *Genre: Urban Arts* under the pseudonym Autumn Ravina Wolf. She has a thing for tea. She can be contacted by emailing hmartinez061301@gmail.com, and wishes you well.

Briana Maytee García is an eighteen-year-old from Los Angeles who is a first-year student at Stanford University. As the daughter of Mexican immigrants, her Hispanic heritage has heavily influenced her goal of heightening societal respect to the Latinx community. A prospective English major, García looks to do her part to aid her community through becoming a lawyer in addition to an author shedding light on the underrepresented. She hopes to one day write a novel that portrays her community as she sees them, not the nefarious outsiders they have depicted as by American society.

Steve Castro's debut poetry collection, *Blue Whale Phenomena,* was published by Otis Books, 2019 (Otis College of Art and Design, Los Angeles, California). Poetry published in *Plume; DIAGRAM; Green Mountains Review; [PANK]; Forklift, Ohio; The Florida Review; Water~Stone Review,* etc. and is forthcoming in Speculative Fiction For Dreamers: A Latinx Anthology (The Ohio State University Press); *Hotel Amerika* and *Guesthouse.* Birthplace: Costa Rica.

Alyssa Noelle Patiño Krull is an undergraduate student at Stanford University, where she plans to study engineering and creative writing. Her maternal side of the family has roots in Michoacán, México, and loves being a part of the Latinx community. Her writing explores topics ranging from cultural and familial identity to scientific questions and phenomena. Outside of her passion for writing, she wants to use engineering to find sustainable energy solutions, while also addressing the importance of environmental justice.

America Garcia loves fashion, film, and writing. She's also a former university student majoring in both theatre and marketing. She plans to become both a fashion designer, film director, and an author. She wants to influence others to not be afraid of pursuing what they want to do. She wants to create change and make an impact in this world.

Ana Lorenza Jimenez is a multi-disciplinary creative who is native to Las Vegas, Nevada. Her family originates from Colombia and Mexico. Ana is a passionate observer and listener who seeks to lead others to experience beauty in ways and places that might otherwise be overlooked. She is currently endeavoring to do this through writing and visual art. She has served in various roles for literary journals such as *Witness* and *Helen: A Literary Magazine*. Her work has been published online and in print for literary arts organizations such as *Royal Rose Magazine*, *Fevers of the Mind Poetry Digest*, *Witness*, *Helen*, and *Nevada Humanities*. She holds an Associates degree in Spanish and is pursuing her Bachelors in Creative Writing at the University of Nevada Las Vegas. Connect with her on Instagram: @anashandsmake.

Gabriella Nayeli Salvador is the author of the poem "When I Learned to Speak Up". She is a proud second-generation Chicana of Zapotec descent. Her poem was inspired by her turbulent experience as a person of indigenous descent in the primarily white educational spaces she grew up in. Gabriella is a first-year student at the University of California, San Diego in the department of Ethnic Studies and looks to serve her Los Angeles community through education and cultural empowerment. Through her poetry, she hopes to create a more inclusive community for the underrepresented intersectional identities within the Latinx community.

Delia Wallace, born in Panama City, Panama, spent most of her days going between Rio Abajo and Juan Diaz as a child. At age 12, she moved to Texas where she lived until the completion of her undergraduate degree at Texas A&M University-Commerce. Following her time in Texas came her move back to Panama, where she is currently studying for her Master's in Sociology and dedicating her time to reconnecting with her roots. Delia Wallace has been writing since she first moved to the United States. For her, writing was the easiest way to make sense of the feelings that came with being an immigrant in a new country and explore all aspects of her newfound identity as an Afro-Latina. Through poetry, Wallace has been able to navigate the intersections of her blackness, Latinidad, queerness, spirituality, and more. She has wholeheartedly embraced her journey and culture, all as an ode to her ancestors.

Theresa Nayelie Palafox is a first generation college graduate with a passion to support and create loving, healing spaces for all students through narrative writing. While being gone from home, she realized the importance of having a strong sense of identity, a foreign concept to her. She spent the rest of her time in Riverside writing poems, short stories, and journals to track her most memorable and most devastating moments in college. Upon completing her degree in Political Science from Riverside, she returned home to Logan Heights and worked with students to develop their best selves mentally, emotionally, and spiritually.

At the core of her Spanglish work, she wants us to feel more connected with each other and be able to embrace the harsh realities than many 1ˢᵗ generation Latinx students do face on their journey of healing and breaking intergenerational patterns. She believes the art of storytelling is a gift that was passed down to many of us from our ancestors, something that she will be forever grateful for.

Cynthia Flores is a third-generation Chicana from Los Angeles. After attending Loyola Marymount University where she earned a BA in Humanities, she attended UC Irvine's Programs in Writing and earned an MFA in Poetry. She also holds a dual emphasis MA in Rhetoric, Composition, and Literature from Cal Poly Pomona. Ms. Flores teaches English and Humanities at Glendale Community College.

German Dario Piedrahita resides in Tempe, Arizona with his wife, two sons, three dogs, a guinea pig, many plants, and sometimes a fish; simply put, with a conference of living things. Recently published work in Gyroscope Review, San Pedro River Review, Good Works Review, Into The Void, The Friday Influence, Right Hand Pointing,

The New Verse News, The Acentos Review, and The American Journal of Poetry.

Jesus Cortez is an undocumented writer and poet from West Anaheim, California. His work is inspired by his upbringing in the city during the violent 1990's, raised by a single mother. Jesus' work has appeared in Harvard Palabritas, Tule Review, the Acentos Review, and Dryland literary journal, among other publications. Through his works, he hopes to shed light on the people and stories about the city that tend to be ignored by the mainstream.

Ednin D. Martinez is a Dominican, Afro-Latinx immigrant, attorney and writer. As a young immigrant in the United States, she is grateful for the many opportunities she was provided and quickly learned she desired to effect change in social justice. She has accomplished this for many years by representing low income and disenfranchised individuals as a Legal Services Staff Attorney, a Public Defender and later an Assistant Prosecutor. However, she has also had a passion for creative writing and hopes that her writing could help others see themselves on the page and realize their stories matter.

To her, being Afro-Latinx means pride. She believes that she could effect change in the world through her writing, not only because of her heritage, but because of what she has endured as an Afro-Latina in the education system as well as the in the legal field. Her background gave her a sensibility and acceptance of people from other backgrounds as well as a hunger to learn about who they are and how they add to the beauty of our diverse American culture. She believes this is what has made the difference in her career, her ability to genuinely connect with the people she served. She now wants to continue to do this through her writing.

In the past ten years, she participated in writing workshops including Gotham, Kweli Journal's, The Art of the Short Story, Vanessa Martir's, Writing Our Lives, and Voices of Our Nation Arts Foundation with authors Evelina Galang and Jaquira Diaz. She wrote a short story which highlights the racial and socio-economic disparities in the Dominican Republic and how those impacted a young girl's immigrant experience in the United States into adulthood. The piece was selected for the fiction writing workshop with Evelenia Galang at

VONA 2015 and earned a scholarship. She also wrote a personal essay which was submitted for the VONA 2020 Memoir class taught by Jaquira Diaz. She is currently enrolled in a six-month memoir writing cohort to continue working on her craft and complete a polished manuscript of her memoir.

Martina Palavecino Bó is an undergraduate student at Universidad Nacional de Tucumán, Argentina. Interested and invested in postcolonial studies and feminism in her country, she hopes to have the means to get a master's degree and eventually a PhD in Latin American Literature.

Eric Ponce is currently a junior at Vanderbilt University studying philosophy and creative writing. Born in Dallas, Texas, Eric was raised by a Mexican-immigrant father and a first-generation Ecuadorian immigrant mother. With a Montessori and International Baccalaureate education, Eric hopes to write and teach fiction for a living, hoping to reconcile his liminal identity with an ever-changing world. He has previously been published in The Vanderbilt Review and This Wonderful World magazine and is excited to be read alongside fellow Latinx authors.

Amaris Castillo is a journalist and the creator of Bodega Stories, a series featuring real stories from the corner store. Her work has appeared in The New York Times, Remezcla, La Galería Magazine, Spanglish Voces, Parents Latina Magazine, and more. Castillo holds a bachelor's degree from the University of South Florida and a master's degree from Columbia University Graduate School of Journalism.

Born in Brooklyn, New York to Dominican parents, Castillo credits the many tales she heard growing up to her lifelong love of storytelling. She lives in Florida with her family.

Sofía Aguilar is a Latina writer, poet, and fourth-year student at Sarah Lawrence College and originally from Los Angeles. Most recently, her work has appeared in *Poetically Mag, Melanin. Magazine,* and *The Westchester Review,* among other publications. She has received the 2018 Nancy Lynn Schwartz Prize for Fiction and is a three-time recipient of the Jean Goldschmidt Kempton Scholarship for Young

Writers for her outstanding contributions to her college community. You can find her at sofiaaguilar.com.

On paper **Janelly Ramos** is a director of operations at a startup. Privately, she is a writer and self-imposed keeper of her family's history. Always the curious child, she fell in love with reading at a young age and credits Sandra Cisnero's The House On Mango Street with being the first novel she saw herself in.

Emerson Machtus was born in Callao, Perú and has worked in the independent film business since very young. He's currently developing new projects and completing films to be released in 2021. He studied Spanish Literature and Journalism at the Universidad Iberoamericana of Mexico City. From a very early age, he's written short stories, poems and screenplays in Spanish and English. He currently lives in Los Angeles, California.

As a Peruvian who's lived in multiple countries and parts of the world, the notions of who (or what) is Latinx in the US is fascinating sociologically to him. The US is the first place where he's ever identified, proudly, as being "Latino".

Daniel Hernández Aldaco brought up in Guadalajara, Mexico. Focuses on public safety and ethnic and racial justice in Mexico. Currently, Daniel is a Policy and Data Analyst for the Seattle Inspector General of Public Safety in police oversight and accountability. Daniel is also exploring art, particularly poetry and filmmaking, as means for justice. Daniel is a 2020 graduate from the master's degree in public policy at Harvard Kennedy School.

Currently, Daniel is a Policy and Statistical Analyst for the Seattle Inspector General of Public Safety, where he supports and leads oversight policy projects. Prior to this position, Daniel worked at the Mexican National Security Commission (2016-2018) as a public policy and research advisor to the Undersecretary of Planning and Forecasting. Daniel has also worked on public safety issues for international public and private organizations, such as the Office of the Inspector General for the New York Police Department (2018) and as a consultant for Innovations for Poverty Action Mexico (2020).

Violeta Orozco is a bilingual Mexican poet and translator who writes in two languages. Author of the poetry books *El cuarto de la luna* (Proyecto Literal 2020), *La edad oscura / As seen by night* Bilingual edition (in press), *The broken woman diaries* (in press). *The broken women diaries* is her debut poetry collection in English, forthcoming in 2021 with the Port Townsend-based press Andante Books. She is a recipient of 2014 José Emilio Pacheco national poetry prize for college students in Mexico. She is also a collaborator of Nueva York Poetry Review, where she translates Latinx poets from English into Spanish in her column "Lenguasuelta". She currently studies a Ph.D. in Hispanic Literature in Rutgers University, researching Chicana poetry and performance. She studied Philosophy and English Literature in UNAM and graduated with an M.A. in Spanish and Linguistics from Ohio University.

Adlyz Caliman is Venezuelan, writer of the books on publication: "*La Cacica*" with Editorial Nueva Luz 21 and "*Cuando el tiempo se detuvo*" with amazon. Contributor in the digital magazine @thewynwoodtimes with the column *Recuerdos en altavoz*. Bachelor of Business Administration, Master of Sciences in Industrial Management, Master in Educational Administration and PHD in Human Sciences. Academic Vice Chancellor at a Private University in Venezuela. Inveterate reader. Educator by conviction.

Yubany Alberto Checo Estévez se graduo de Ingeniería Telemática en la Pontificia Universidad Católica Madre y Maestra, de electrónica en Hesston College y con maestría en administración de Sistemas de Información en el Steven Institute of Technology. Ha tomado cursos de escritura académica en la Universidad de Duke y talleres de escritura creativa en el Taller Literario Narradores de Santo Domingo (TLNSD) del cual forma parte. Tiene publicaciones en la revista deportiva digital MasTKD. Ganador del concurso de poemas a las madres de la emisora Vida FM y primer lugar del proyecto de La idea al objeto con su colección publicada de cuentos *Pequeñas Sombras Humanas* (disponible en Amazon).

Miembro de la Asociación Dominicana de Ficción Especulativa. Ha publicado sus cuentos en la revista
digital MiNatura, en el Winter Writing Contest de Short Fiction Break en USA, en el Cuarto libro del taller
de escritura Móntame una Escena en España y en la antología Se nos fue poniendo viernes la tarde del
Taller Literario Narradores de Santo Domingo, en la revista Letralia y en la convocatoria 2020 S.O.S. Antologador de los cuentos premiados del Taller Literario Narradores de Santo Domingo con la obra Sombrero para gatos y de la obra de ficción especulativa de la Asociación Dominicana de Ficción Especulativa (ADFE) De Galipotes y Robots. Subcoordinador del Taller Literario Narradores de Santo Domingo en 2018.

Ganador del tercer lugar del concurso Internacional de Cuentos Casa De Teatro en 2108, tercera mención del primer concurso de cuentos Juan Bosch del TLNSD y segundo lugar del concurso de micro ficción Lauro Zavala. Mención de honor del Concurso de Cuentos Alianza Cibaeña en 2019. Ganador en 2018 y 2019 del National Novel Writing Month (Nanowrimo). Cultiva los géneros fantástico, horror y ciencia ficción. Amante de las películas, deportes, música, locución y tecnología.

Graciela Matrajt es escritora amateur además de ser científica y profesora de español, francés y ciencia. Radica en la ciudad de Seattle, WA, EE. UU. desde 2004. Graciela nació en 1972 en Argentina. Es Mexicana y se graduó de la Universidad Nacional Autónoma de México (UNAM) como bióloga. Obtuvo su maestría y doctorado en la Universidad de París, Francia. Graciela ha publicado varios artículos científicos así como perfiles y comentarios sobre ciencia, que se pueden leer en su sitio web https://sites.google.com/site/gracielamatrajt/home. Desde hace unos meses se dedica también a escribir ficción a través de mini cuentos.

Paola Klug es escritora mexicana de ascendencia chinanteca y guatemalteca, nacida en Tecolutla, Veracruz. Hija de un afromexicano y nieta de mujeres valientes. Autodidácta. Sus obras se centran en la cultura popular mexicana, el mestizaje y el realismo mágico.

ACKNOWLEDGEMENTS

Rosa Flores would like to give thanks to her family and teachers who have constantly guided her in her growth.

Ryan Morillo would like thanks his parents for their endless support.

Daniela Bolanos would like to give thanks to her family and friends.

Joselyn Vera would like to give thanks to su Amá, su Apá, her siblings, y el Rockyfelio y la Fifis.

Yasmeen Alfaqueeh would like to thank her family for their love, especially her mother who taught her the beauty of literature.

Noelle Castro would like to give thanks to Victoria Castro, John Groenhoff, Cody Groenhoff, Angelo Castro, and the entire Castro Family

Ada Cruz would like to the amazing PALABRITAS team and all the writers who made this publications possible.

Fatima Reyes would like to give thanks to her incredibly hard-working parents, her brother Diego, and her sister Fernanda.

Emily Rios would like to give thanks to her high school teacher and mentor, Jennifer Olmeda, for her continued support and giving her the space to express herself.

ABOUT PALABRITAS

PALABRITAS is a Latinx literary publication based out of Harvard College with the mission of creating a space for Latinx writers to showcase their work, regardless of prior publishing experience. Thus, our goal is to publish intriguing work by authors that have published before alongside others who've never shared their work publicly. We publish all kinds of creative writing: poetry, short fiction, memoir, personal essay, creative non-fiction, and pieces that don't quite fit a mold. We welcome Latinx authors of any age, background, and experience. Our debut issue was published in the Fall of 2018.

Made in the USA
Columbia, SC
18 June 2021